VIETNAM STUDIES

TACTICAL AND MATERIEL INNOVATIONS

by

Lieutenant General John H. Hay, Jr.

DEPARTMENT OF THE ARMY

WASHINGTON, D.C., 1974

Library of Congress Catalog Card Number: 72-600390

First Printing

For sale by the Superintendent of Documents, U.S. Government Printing Office
Washington, D.C. 20402 - Price $2.20 (paper cover)
Stock Number 0820-00471

Foreword

The United States Army has met an unusually complex challenge in Southeast Asia. In conjunction with the other services, the Army has fought in support of a national policy of assisting an emerging nation to develop governmental processes of its own choosing, free of outside coercion. In addition to the usual problems of waging armed conflict, the assignment in Southeast Asia has required superimposing the immensely sophisticated tasks of a modern army upon an underdeveloped environment and adapting them to demands covering a wide spectrum. These involved helping to fulfill the basic needs of an agrarian population, dealing with the frustrations of antiguerrilla operations, and conducting conventional campaigns against well-trained and determined regular units.

It is as always necessary for the U.S. Army to continue to prepare for other challenges that lie ahead. While cognizant that history never repeats itself exactly and that no army every profited from trying to meet a new challenge in terms of the old one, the Army nevertheless stands to benefit immensely from a study of its experience, its shortcomings no less than its achievements.

Aware that some years must elapse before the official histories will provide a detailed and objective analysis of the experience in Southeast Asia, we have sought a forum whereby some of the more salient aspects of that experience can be made available now. At the request of the Chief of Staff, a representative group of senior officers who served in important posts in Vietnam and who still carry a heavy burden of day-to-day responsibilities has prepared a series of monographs. These studies should be of great value in helping the Army develop future operational concepts while at the same time contributing to the historical record and providing the American public with an interim report on the performance of men and officers who have responded, as others have through our history, to exacting and trying demands.

The reader should be reminded that most of the writing was accomplished while the war in Vietnam was at its peak, and the monographs frequently refer to events of the past as if they were taking place in the present.

All monographs in the series are based primarily on official records, with additional material from published and unpublished secondary works, from debriefing reports and interviews with key participants, and from the personal experience of the author. To facilitate security clearance, annotation and detailed bibliography have been omitted from the published version; a fully documented account with bibliography is filed with the Office of the Chief of Military History.

The qualifications of Lieutenant General John H. Hay, Jr., to write *Tactical and Materiel Innovations* are considerable. After graduating from the Advanced Management Program at Harvard University, General Hay served as the Army Member, Military Studies and Liaison Division, Weapons Systems Evaluation Group, Office of the Secretary of Defense, from December 1962 to June 1964. General Hay was then assigned as the Commanding General, Berlin Brigade, in West Berlin, Germany, from July 1964 until August 1966, at which time he became the Commanding General, 11th Infantry Brigade, U.S. Army, Pacific, September 1966-January 1967. In February 1967 he became the Commanding General of the 1st Infantry Division in Vietnam and held this position until March 1968, when he was reassigned as Deputy Commanding General, II Field Force, Vietnam, responsible for the defense of Saigon. He left Vietnam in August 1968. On 5 September 1968 he assumed the dual position of Commandant of the U.S. Army Command and General Staff College, Fort Leavenworth, Kansas, and Commanding General of the U.S. Army Combat Development Command Institute of Combined Arms and Support. This latter position together with his combat experience in Vietnam and earlier assignment with the Weapons System Evaluation Group make General Hay uniquely qualified to be the author of this study. General Hay is currently the Commanding General of the XVIII Airborne Corps at Fort Bragg, North Carolina.

Washington, D.C.
1 May 1973

VERNE L. BOWERS
Major General, USA
The Adjutant General

Preface

I was the commandant of the U.S. Army Command and General Staff College when General William C. Westmoreland asked me to prepare this monograph. The official archives there, as well as the availability of the college staff, permitted a greater depth of research and analysis than would otherwise have been possible. We limited our study to innovations which influence the command of an infantry division. My guidance to my assistants was to write for a professional audience, but to make the monograph readable and interesting for the general public. Battle stories are used to illustrate both tactical and materiel innovations.

The study covers only a few of the thousands of innovations which have occurred in Vietnam. However, I think that it serves to define the constant challenge to our soldiers at every level of the Army: to stay ahead of the many changes which are evolving in our profession at this time in our history.

Washington, D.C.
1 May 1973

JOHN H. HAY, JR.
Lieutenant General, U.S. Army

Contents

Chapter		Page
I.	INTRODUCTION	3
II.	IA DRANG	10
III.	IRVING	24
IV.	LOC NINH	42
V.	REMAGEN AND MONTANA MAULER	57
VI.	CORONADO X	66
VII.	DAK TO	78
VIII.	FIRE SUPPORT BASE CROOK FIRE SUPPORT SURVEILLANCE BASE FLOYD	97
IX.	TAM KY	107
X.	PHONG CAO	117
XI.	SUOI CAT	127
XII.	LAM SON II	137
XIII.	CU CHI	148
XIV.	VINH LOC AND PHU VANG I	162
XV.	SEARCH AND DESTROY	169
XVI.	SUMMARY	179
GLOSSARY		185
INDEX		189

Charts

No.		
1.	Three Phases of Vietnam Strategy	172
2.	Vietnamese and Allied Forces in South Vietnam	175
3.	Population Status in South Vietnam	181

Maps

1. Battles Illustrated 4
2. Types of Terrain in South Vietnam 7

Diagrams

No.		Page
1.	Rifle Company Cloverleafs, Advancing Toward Contact	44
2.	Fire Support Surveillance Base FLOYD Layout, 29 August 1970	102
3.	Schematic Deployment of Two Rifle Companies and Reconnaissance Platoon in Checkerboard Search Pattern	118
4.	Location of Firefight	121

Illustrations

Huey Cobra Firing Rockets at Enemy Target 14
CH-47 Chinook 15
Firefly Illumination System 21
YO-3A Quiet Aircraft 23
CH-54 "Flying Crane" 28
Members of an Engineer Tunnel Rat Team 35
Riot Hand Grenade 37
Dust-off Helicopter Hoists Wounded Man 40
Scout Dog Leads Patrol 46
CIDG Compound and Loc Ninh Airstrip 47
Sergeant and Rifleman Engage Enemy With M16 Rifles 50
Claymore Mine 52
General William C. Westmoreland and Major General John H. Hay, Jr. 55
UH-1 Helicopter Makes Delivery 61
500-Gallon Collapsible Drums Filled With Fuel 62
Armored Vehicle Launched Bridge 65
USS *Benewah* 67
Eagle Float of Mobile Riverine Force 71
Barge-mounted 105-mm. Howitzer 73
Mock-up of XM-2 Airborne Personnel Detector 81
AN/ASC-15 Communication Central 83
Bulldozers With Rome Plows Clear Jungle Growth 88
Result of Defoliation Operations 93
Fire Support Base CROOK 98
Aerial Delivered Seismic Intrusion Detector 105
Starlight Scope 106
Armored Cavalry Assault Vehicles With RPG Screens 109
Armored Personnel Carriers Clear the Way 110
"General Sheridan" 113
Combat Engineer Vehicle 114

Page

Soldiers Training on Troop Ladders 125
M48 Tanks Halted in Herringbone Formation 129
Engineer Mine Clearing Team 133
ENSURE 202 Roller on M48 Tank 135
1st Infantry Division Band Performing at Tan Phuoc Khanh 138
Woman Wins Yorkshire Pig 139
Villagers Receive Treatment During MEDCAP 140
Loudspeaker Team Broadcasts Propaganda Message 144
Personalized Propaganda Leaflet 145
Scenes Around Cu Chi Base Camp 152
Special Services Activities at Cu Chi Base Camp 153
Interior of Univac 1005 Computer Van 158
Recovery of Downed Helicopter by CH-47 160
ARVN Soldiers and U.S. Adviser 165
Prisoners of War Are Taken to Collection Point 166
Infantry Troops Searching Enemy Base Area 174

Illustrations are from Department of Defense files.

TACTICAL AND MATERIEL INNOVATIONS

CHAPTER I

Introduction

For the U.S. Army, the war in Vietnam presented a new type of battle fought with new weapons and new tactics against a very different enemy. In many respects, the area war without front lines together with the guerrilla tactics were out of our nation's beginnings, while the sophisticated hardware presaged the future automated battlefield management systems.

This monograph discusses some of the more important tactical and materiel innovations in Vietnam from the viewpoint of the infantry division commander. A few well-documented battles illustrate new concepts and hardware, most of which were developed over an extended period of time in a variety of operations. (*Map 1*) However, the basic tactical doctrine has not changed; it has merely been expanded by new capabilities or altered to the Vietnam situation.

The tactics and methods of the North Vietnamese and Viet Cong soldiers did not fit the patterns established by enemy forces in World War II and the Korean War. This fact was especially evident during the stages of the insurgency when the enemy's main force units tried to avoid heavy contact in favor of terrorism and ambush. Another difference was that all of South Vietnam was a war arena with shifting scenes of combat in comparison to the rigidity imposed by the narrow front lines characteristic of past conflicts.

U.S. tactics, however, adjusted to the situation. In a land that favored the easily hidden, lightly loaded foot soldier, the helicopter balanced the odds. Airmobility was a dramatic new dimension, which allowed the precise application of a variety of combat power. Finally, pacification became a new consideration for the combat commander, one which did not concern him in the past.

Many of the tactical and materiel innovations developed in Vietnam were in response to the enemy's methods of operation in Southeast Asia. The key military strategy of the North Vietnamese Army (NVA) and the Viet Cong (VC) was to retain the initiative through offensive action. They intended to avoid allied strongpoints and to attack the weak spots of their choice. While they made many deliberate attacks against allied positions, they tended to favor three basic tactical operations: the raid, the ambush, and the attack by fire. The purpose of these attacks was to inflict casualties and to destroy equipment and installations, although at times the enemy's objectives were

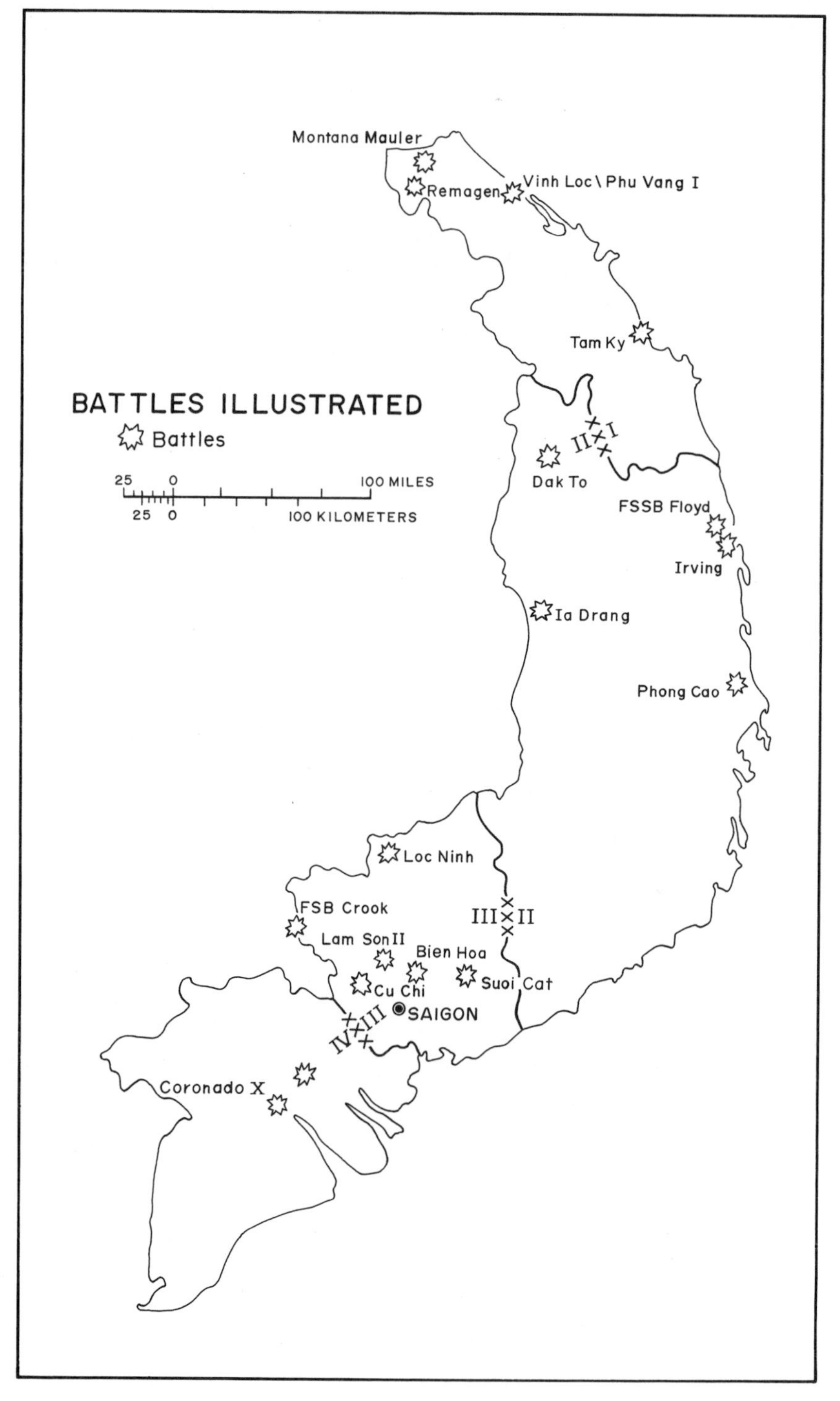
Montana Mauler
Remagen
Vinh Loc\Phu Vang I
Tam Ky
BATTLES ILLUSTRATED
Battles
25
0
100 MILES
25
0
100 KILOMETERS
II
I
Dak To
FSSB Floyd
Irving
Ia Drang
Phong Cao
Loc Ninh
FSB Crook
III
II
Lam Son II
Bien Hoa
Cu Chi
Suoi Cat
SAIGON
IV
III
Coronado X

MAP 1

purely political or psychological. After U.S. forces were introduced in South Vietnam in 1965, the enemy realized that to occupy, hold, or deny strategic positions was beyond his capability. The only ground that he held with any degree of permanence was in the sanctuaries across the border in Cambodia, Laos, and North Vietnam.

The North Vietnamese Army and the Viet Cong normally defended by evading. Only occasionally would they defend a position as a feint or deception, trying to draw allied forces into a trap or to divert them from a larger unit nearby. Enemy tacticians recognized that the allied forces were superior in firepower and mobility. To overcome this superiority, the enemy attempted to mass, attack, and withdraw before allied forces could react. Each of the enemy's operations was planned in minute detail and often rehearsed.

The enemy's combat forces were lightly equipped so that they could move more freely and quickly. They could not depend upon the type of supply lines used by most conventional forces. Instead, they brought supplies in before the battle and positioned them ahead of time. Extra weapons and ammunition were cached near the objective. Medical supplies, ammunition, and food were stored along the withdrawal routes. Thus, an increase in the movement of supplies and in the discovery of caches was a fairly reliable indication of an impending enemy offensive operation.

The survival of the enemy forces on the battlefield depended on their ability to disengage from or avoid contact with allied forces. They considered the withdrawal phase of the operation as important as any other combat action. When necessary, they would counterattack in an attempt to disengage. If routes leading away from the battlefield were blocked, the enemy troops would try to attack a weak spot in the allied position and escape through the breach. Delaying forces would ambush and harass pursuers. If an orderly withdrawal was not possible, small unit commanders would disperse their troops in the hope of rendezvousing later at a predesignated point.

Very early in the Vietnam War, U.S. forces realized that finding the elusive enemy would tax intelligence resources to the limit. Traditional methods of collecting, analyzing, and disseminating information were too slow to provide the timely intelligence needed. U.S. forces expanded techniques developed in earlier conflicts, such as pattern analysis and long-range patrols, but these were not enough. Equipment such as acoustic, magnetic, and seismic sensors, platforms for airborne reconnaissance, and surveillance and observation devices was rapidly developed. Close co-ordination between intelligence activities and the operational forces took on new meaning as efforts were made to react to information while it was still useful. In past wars, U.S. forces pieced together the enemy picture and coupled it with considerations of terrain, weather, and objectives; in Vietnam, however, the enemy was pursued as soon as his position was reasonably certain.

The area war, in contrast to the traditional division of territory between friendly and enemy forces, had a radical effect on every aspect of military operations. Widely distributed, semipermanent logistic complexes and base camps were connected by aerial supply routes and armed convoys. These installations, defended from attack by the troops who lived there, provided administrative, logistic, and combat support to sustain the maneuver battalions. Adequate area coverage by artillery batteries required many fortified fire support bases. These compact defensive circles supported infantry, mechanized, cavalry, and tank units and were in turn protected by them. The infantry battalions, companies, and platoons were usually on the offensive, digging in at night in carefully planned night defensive positions. The daily operation map, instead of showing a precise line of contact, was sprinkled with red and blue symbols throughout the area of operation. Instead of a barren no man's land between adversaries, the battle was often waged in a well-populated countryside. The enemy hid easily among a people so intimidated as to prove all too often an unreliable source of information. On the allied side, special rules of engagement regulated the use of combat power in order to avoid casualties among the civilian population.

The helicopter was extremely important. Introduced first in Korea, it added new dimensions to warfare. In Vietnam it extended the infantry unit's area of control at least threefold. A commander could react to opportunities quicker, delay his decision, or even change his plan en route. He could pile on, block escape routes, extract, or surprise. His entire unit could be shifted to a new area on short notice. At times he was completely free from considerations of terrain. In the airmobile division, the helicopter was totally integrated into all operations. Without the helicopter in Vietnam, limited numbers of allied forces would not have been able to outmaneuver the enemy nor to exercise their superiority of firepower.

The terrain and weather in different areas of Vietnam greatly influenced the character of the war and led the tactical commander to develop his own methods of fighting. In the Mekong Delta, extensive flat rice paddies and swamps, often impassable for vehicles, are laced with canals and streams. Riverine tactics, using special shallow-draft gunboats, floating artillery, and armored transports, assisted ground forces in battles against the firmly entrenched Viet Cong. (*Map 2*)

The piedmont area around Saigon consists of gently rolling hills and broad plains. It bordered well-stocked Cambodian sanctuaries and included the infamous jungle bases War Zones C and D. Well suited for tracked vehicle movement, the area was the scene of many main force battles.

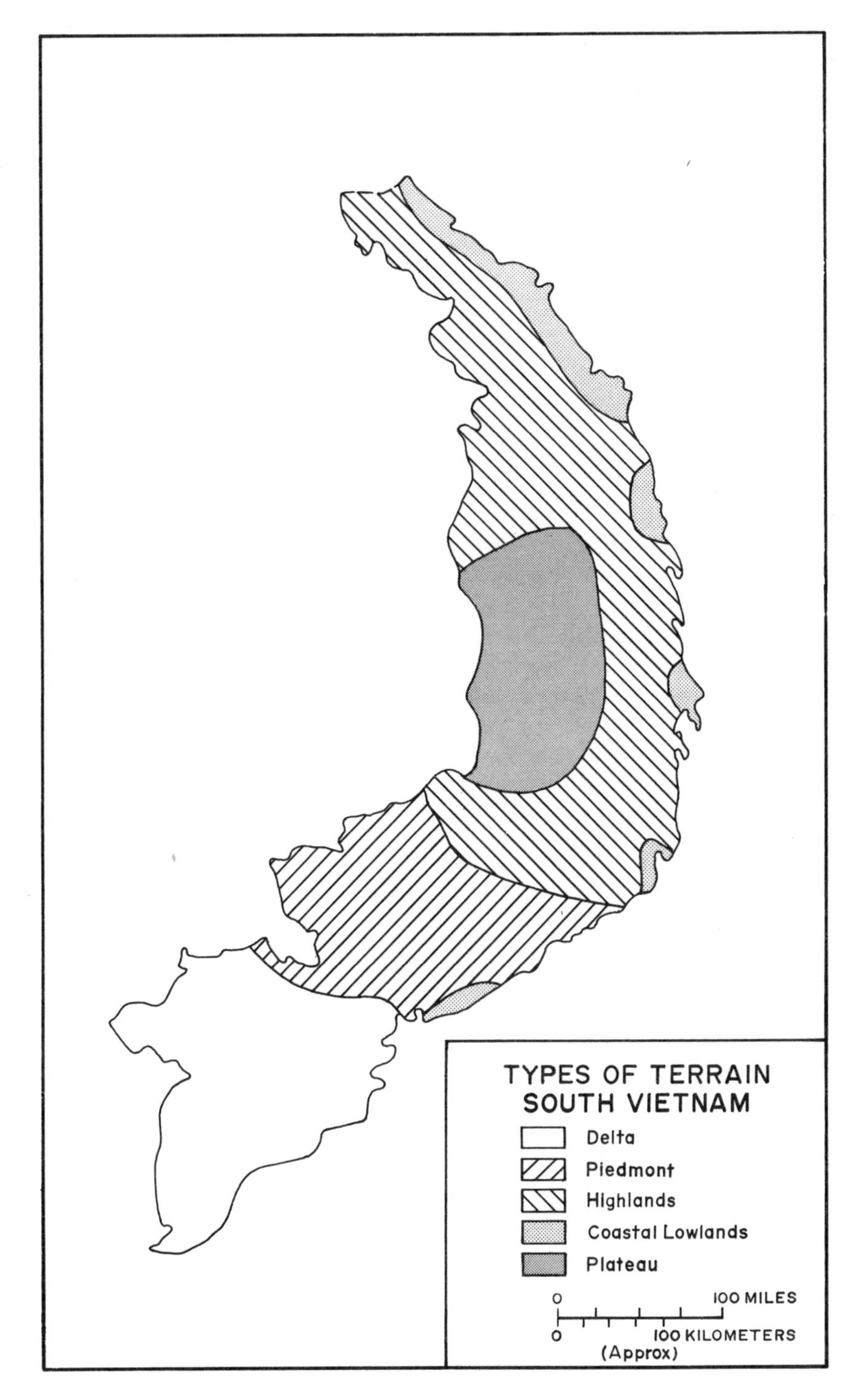
TYPES OF TERRAIN
SOUTH VIETNAM
Delta
Piedmont
Highlands
Coastal Lowlands
Plateau
0
100 MILES
0
100 KILOMETERS
(Approx)

MAP 2

The narrow coastal plains of the northern half of South Vietnam are characterized by sandy beaches, wide flat river valleys, marshes, and rice fields. Much of the population, commerce, and agriculture as well as many U.S. logistic bases and headquarters were concentrated in these areas. They were tempting targets for the enemy, therefore, and required special protection to avoid casualties among U.S. troops and their allies during combat operations.

The rugged mountains with dense forests are broken by a rolling plateau from Pleiku to Ban Me Thuot. Tracked vehicle movement and helicopter landings here were severely limited. Poor weather and the great distance from supply centers were important limiting factors. Enemy forces in the highlands were mainly regular units of the North Vietnamese Army.

The country is mostly hot, humid, and tropical. Heavy annual rainfall—120 inches on the northern coastline, 80 inches in Saigon, and 40 inches at Phan Rang—comes with the monsoons to the north of the mountains in the winter months and to the Mekong Delta and piedmont area in the summer. Observation, off-road movement, aerial flight, and communications deteriorated during the monsoon seasons. Maintenance, supply, and storage problems increased and the incidence of disease went up. Enemy activity was usually lower during the wet seasons.

U.S. fire support in the form of artillery, tactical air, heavy bombers, and helicopter gunships was superior to that of the enemy, whose fire support normally consisted of mortars, rockets, and recoilless rifles. The enemy often tried to "hug" allied ground forces at ranges too close for the use of heavy weapons. U.S. and allied tactics centered around detailed reconnaissance, airmobile maneuver, and overwhelming firepower. Defensively, the meticulously planned fire support bases and night defensive positions of the U.S. forces became impregnable strongpoints. Unlike previous wars, there were very few objectives of terrain for allied forces. The enemy unit, wherever it was located in South Vietnam, was the target.

Pacification as a primary mission demanded new considerations from a combat commander. All offensive and security operations were undertaken within the broader goal of restoring the control of the Republic of Vietnam government over the population. U.S. combat units joined with Vietnamese forces and local government organizations to weed out the Viet Cong infrastructure, reopen roads, re-establish markets, build schools, and give medical care to the needy. The credit for such operations was given to local government leaders whenever possible.

A Korean War veteran would recognize the steel helmet, the pistol, the mortars, the towed howitzers, and the jerry can. The rest of today's hardware is new. The old mess kit is gone; troops are fed on trays or paper plates. The lightweight M16 rifle has replaced the old M1, and the M79 grenade launcher, the light antitank weapon, and the claymore mine have increased the infantryman's firepower. The helicopter, improved communications, and the management of available fire support have greatly magnified the combat power of U.S. units. The armored personnel carrier, the Sheridan, and the Huey helicopter are newly developed vehicles. The latest sensors, automatic data processing systems, and advanced management techniques are steps into the future.

CHAPTER II

Ia Drang (October-November 1965)

The battle of Ia Drang illustrates the influence of the helicopter on combat operations. It also demonstrates the usefulness of new organizations such as the air cavalry, with its greatly increased ability to locate and fight the enemy, and the airmobile division, with its great advance in mobility. The expanded role of Army aircraft is seen in such refinements as the use of the gunship and the tactical employment of airmobile troops. The battle story introduces a series of innovations developed before and during the Vietnam War.

There has been some speculation as to how the war would have been waged without the helicopter. General Westmoreland answered the question in this way:

> Suppose that we did not have helicopters and airmobile divisions today. How many troops would we have needed to accomplish what we have achieved in South Vietnam? . . . No finite answer is possible because our tactics in Vietnam were based on massive use of helicopters. . . . What would we do without helicopters? We would be fighting a different war, for a smaller area, at a greater cost, with less effectiveness. We might as well have asked: 'What would General Patton have done without his tanks?'

The helicopter was first used in combat by U.S. armed forces for medical evacuation during the Korean War. Although many helicopter assault techniques were later developed by the U.S. Army and Marine Corps, it was the findings of the Howze Board, the formation of the 11th Air Assault Division, and the development of small turbine engines that first brought airmobility into its own.

The first airmobile division was sent to Vietnam in the third quarter of 1965 as the 1st Cavalry Division (Airmobile). After establishing a base at An Khe in the II Corps Tactical Zone and conducting a few operations against local Viet Cong forces, the division showed its strength in the Ia Drang Valley in the fall of 1965.

On 19 October the enemy attacked a Civilian Irregular Defense Group (CIDG) camp at Plei Me—the opening bid in an attempt to take over the Central Highlands. By 22 October intelligence indicated that there were two North Vietnamese Army regiments in the area: the 33d Regiment, at Plei Me, and the 32d Regiment, which was waiting in ambush to destroy the expected relief column from Pleiku, north of Plei Me.

The Vietnamese II Corps commander was confronted with a difficult choice. He could refuse to go to the relief of Plei Me and lose the camp, or he could commit the reserve from Pleiku, stripping the area of defensive troops. If he lost the reserve, Pleiku would be easy prey for the Communists, who could then control the western part of the Central Highlands. He decided to ask for help from the U.S. forces. The Commanding General, Field Forces, Vietnam, Major General Stanley R. Larsen, sent the following message to Major General Harry W. O. Kinnard, Commanding General, 1st Cavalry Division: "Commencing first light 23 October First Air Cav deploys one Bn TF minimum 1 Inf Bn and 1 Arty Btry to PLEIKU, mission be prepared to assist in defense of key US/ARVN installations vic PLEIKU or reinforce II Corps operations to relieve PLEI ME CIDG CAMP."

Task Force INGRAM was airlifted from An Khe to Pleiku early on 23 October. The force consisted of the 2d Battalion, 12th Cavalry, reinforced with a battery of artillery. While the move was under way, the division commander, sensing that a decisive operation was imminent at Plei Me, obtained permission to deploy the 1st Brigade to Pleiku. The brigade headquarters with the 2d Battalion, 8th Cavalry, and two batteries of the 2d Battalion, 19th Artillery, arrived by air at Camp Holloway by midnight on 23 October to assume operational control of Task Force INGRAM. The 1st Brigade was charged with securing Pleiku, providing artillery support for the Vietnamese Army's relief of Plei Me, and furnishing a reserve force.

Meanwhile, the ARVN (Army of the Republic of Vietnam) armored relief column began moving down Provincial Road 6C toward Plei Me. At 1730 hours the North Vietnamese Army struck the relief column at two points, but 1st Cavalry artillery was called in on the ambushing enemy with deadly accuracy and was a decisive factor in repulsing the attack.

Before the relief column arrived at Plei Me, the camp had been resupplied day and night by airdrops from the Army's CV-2 (Caribou) of the 92d Aviation Company, the CV-7 (Buffalo) of the U.S. Army Aviation Test Board, and the Air Force's C-123. On the night of 24 October the weather was overcast and the camp could not be seen from the air. In order to identify a release point on which to drop the parachute loads, the camp commander fired a star-burst flare straight up through the overcast, and the pilots released their loads using the flare as a reference point. Most of the ammunition and food landed within the compound.

On the evening of 25 October the relief column arrived at the camp, which was still under siege, and immediately reinforced the defensive perimeter. By then, 1st Cavalry infantry and artillery had air-assaulted from Pleiku into landing zones within close support range. The original enemy plan to destroy the ARVN relief column and then fall on Plei Me had failed. At 2220 hours on 25 October, the 33d North Vietnamese Army Regiment at Plei Me was ordered to withdraw to the west, leaving behind a reinforced battalion to cover the withdrawal.

At this point General William C. Westmoreland visited the 1st Brigade's forward command post and directed the 1st Cavalry Division to pursue and destroy the enemy. The division's scope of operations changed from reinforcement and reaction to unlimited offense. The division was to be responsible for searching out and destroying all enemy forces that threatened the Central Highlands. The 1st Brigade pursued the battle through 9 November. The 3d Brigade took over until 20 November, when the 2d Brigade began the final operation.

The battlefield covered 1,500 square miles of generally flat to rolling terrain drained by an extensive network of rivers and small streams flowing to the west and southwest across the border into Cambodia. The dominating feature of the terrain was the Chu Pong massif in the southwestern corner of the area, straddling the Cambodian-Vietnamese frontier. For long periods this mountain mass had been an important enemy infiltration area and one of the many strongholds where enemy forces could mass and construct strong defenses under the heavily canopied jungle.

Intelligence indicated that a field front (divisional headquarters) was controlling the enemy regiments. If so, this operation marked the first time any U.S. unit in Vietnam had opposed a division-size unit of the North Vietnamese Army under a single commander.

The first significant contact was made on 1 November, when a platoon of Troop B, 1st Squadron, 9th Cavalry, overran a regimental aid station six miles southwest of Plei Me, killing fifteen enemy soldiers and capturing fifteen more. This rifle platoon had been air-assaulted into the area in response to reports that scattered groups of enemy soldiers had been sighted. Two more rifle platoons from A and B Troops were landed to sweep through the area. Just after 1400 hours, scout helicopters discovered a battalion-size enemy force moving from the northeast toward the U.S. platoons. The fighting intensified at ranges too close for aerial rocket artillery or tactical air support. The position was also beyond the range of available tube artillery. Reinforcement platoons from the 1st and 2d Battalions of the 12th Cavalry and the 2d Battalion of the 8th Cavalry landed late in the afternoon, followed by two additional platoons from the 2d Battalion, 12th Cavalry. Ground fire was intense on all reinforcement, resupply, and evacuation helicopters, and seven ships were hit by enemy fire. By 1700 hours Company B, 1st Battalion, 8th Cavalry, was committed to the battle, and by 1900 hours the platoons of the 9th Cavalry Squadron, having found and fixed the enemy, were airlifted from the area.

By the time the enemy was driven from the field the 33d North Vietnamese Army Regiment had lost its aid station, many patients, and over $40,000 worth of important medical supplies and had sustained 99 men killed and 183 wounded.

The airmobile concept had proved itself. Scout ships would reconnoiter and locate enemy groups, rifle elements would fix the enemy in place, and heliborne units, supported by massed air and ground firepower, would attack and defeat the enemy troops. These tactics worked successfully again and again during the battle.

In a well-executed ambush at 2100 hours on 3 November, the rifle platoons of the 1st Squadron, 9th Cavalry, again drew blood. Troops in one of several ambush positions located just north of the Chu Pong Mountain sighted a heavily laden North Vietnamese Army unit, estimated at company strength, moving along an east-west trail. Deciding to take a break just one hundred meters short of the ambush site, the enemy column loitered outside the killing zone for ninety minutes, while the U.S. troops waited quietly in ambush. At 2100 hours the enemy unit moved noisily along the trail. The first element was allowed to pass, and then the trap was sprung with eight claymores along a 100-meter zone. The attack was perfectly executed and the enemy's weapons platoon with machine guns, mortars, and recoilless rifles was caught in a wall of lead as the cavalrymen fired continuously for two minutes. There was no return fire.

The ambush patrol returned immediately to its base and went to work strengthening its perimeter. By 2230 hours the base was under heavy attack by an estimated two or three companies of North Vietnamese Army regulars. At midnight the perimeter was in grave danger of being overrun, but reinforcements were on the way. Company A, 1st Battalion, 8th Cavalry, standing by at the Duc Co Special Forces Camp, located twelve miles of roadless jungle to the north, had been alerted. The first platoon was on the ground and in combat forty minutes after midnight. The entire company had arrived by 0240 hours. While this type of relief and reinforcement is now routine, it was unique in November 1965. This battle marked the first time a perimeter under heavy fire was reinforced at night by heliborne troops air-assaulted into an unfamiliar landing zone. It was also the first time that aerial rocket artillery was used at night and as close as fifty meters to U.S. troops.

By dawn the enemy attack had lost momentum, and the fighting diminished to occasional sniping from surrounding trees. As a result of the battle, ninety-eight North Vietnamese soldiers were killed and ten were captured. In addition, over 100,000 rounds of 7.62-mm. ammunition, two 82-mm. mortars, and three 75-mm. recoilless rifles were destroyed, and large quantities of mortar and recoilless rifle ammunition were captured. The implications of an ambush deep within

HUEY COBRA FIRING ROCKETS AT ENEMY TARGET

what was thought to be secure territory must have stunned the North Vietnamese Army's high command.

Although the helicopter was no longer strange to the enemy, he had failed to appreciate its use in tactical roles other than as a prime mover of supplies and men. For the first time the enemy found his withdrawal routes blocked, his columns attacked, and artillery fire directed on his routes of escape—all because of the new dimension added to the war by aggressive tactical use of the helicopter. During the pursuit of the 33d North Vietnamese Army Regiment from Plei Me, the enemy was so baffled by the constant harassment and rapid compromises of "secure" way stations that the North Vietnamese Army command concluded that there were traitors in the regiment providing target information to the Americans.

Arming Army aircraft had been tried as far back as the 1950s, but the war in Vietnam brought about an intensive program to develop Army aircraft weapons. In 1962 at Nha Trang, the 23d Special Warfare Aviation Detachment (Surveillance), whose mission was to support provincial forces, tested six OV-1A Mohawks armed with .50-caliber machine guns and 2.75-inch folding-fin aerial rockets. This successful program was expanded until 1966, when Army fixed-wing aircraft were taken out of the fighter-escort mission by the Department of Defense. No approved armament program was established.

During this same period, the use of armed helicopters increased rapidly. In October 1962, the Utility Tactical Transportation Com-

CH-47 Chinook

pany (the Army's first armed helicopter unit) equipped with UH-1A's replaced B-26's and T-28's as escorts for CH-21 (Shawnee) troop helicopters. Losses decreased significantly. By May 1964, B-model Hueys (UH-1B) had replaced the CH-21 for carrying troops, and ten light airmobile aviation companies, with one to three armed platoons each, were in Vietnam. In 1965 the 1st Cavalry Division (Airmobile) brought the first air cavalry squadron and aerial artillery battalion to the Republic of Vietnam. Three armed Chinooks (CH-47A) were tested in 1966, but the arrival of the Cobra (AH-1G) ended that project. The Huey Cobra was introduced in 1968 with 75 percent more ordnance and 30 percent more speed than any of the Huey gunships. By April 1969, over half of the 680 helicopters in Vietnam were Cobras.

There were five types of U.S. Army units operating in South Vietnam which were authorized to use armed helicopters: assault helicopter companies (nondivision), attack helicopter companies (airmobile division and nondivision), general support companies (infantry division), aerial rocket artillery battalions (airmobile division), and air cavalry troops (nondivision, divisional, armored cavalry regiment). Armed helicopter missions were primarily oriented to support ground maneuver forces. On such a mission, the helicopter's functions were to provide security and to deliver firepower. There were five categories of missions in which armed helicopters were commonly used: armed escort of other aircraft, surface vehicles and vessels, and personnel on the ground; security for an observation helicopter performing low-level reconnaissance; direct fire support against targets assigned by a commander of a ground maneuver element; aerial rocket artillery functions against targets assigned by a fire support coordination center, forward observer, or airborne commander; and hunter-killer tactics to provide security for an observation helicopter performing low-level reconnaissance and to deliver firepower on targets of opportunity.

One of the most significant tactical innovations to come out of early U.S. efforts in Vietnam was the "eagle flight." The exact origin of the term is obscure, but it dates from the period in late 1962 when the five U.S. CH-21 helicopter companies transporting ARVN forces were joined by the first company of armed UH-1 helicopters—the Utility Tactical Transport Helicopter Company. An elite ARVN platoon was mounted in five CH-21's and escorted by two to five armed Hueys. The gunships provided suppressive fire in the landing zone and conducted aerial reconnaissance to locate the enemy. The infantry could be landed to engage a small enemy force, check a hamlet, or pick up suspects for questioning, while the gunships provided support. If nothing was found, the troops would be picked up and the operation repeated again in another likely location. The eagle flight contributed greatly to ARVN operations. As one report stated, "The enemy can fade away before the large formations, but he never knows where the 'Eagle Flight' will land next." The success of these early operations demonstrated the feasibility of airmobile tactics in actual combat, promoted the idea of armed helicopters, and paved the way for the development of much larger air assault forces. Such practical experience was infused in the testing of the airmobile concept by the 11th Air Assault Division.

The variety of aircraft organic to air cavalry permitted maximum flexibility in organizing for combat and enabled the commander to structure the assets into teams to satisfy mission requirements. One air cavalry troop was organic to the armored cavalry squadron of the infantry division, and three were organic to the air cavalry squadron of the airmobile division. Each troop consisted of a scout platoon equipped with light observation helicopters, an aerial weapons platoon with AH-1G armed helicopters, and a rifle platoon with organic UH-1H utility helicopters. In Vietnam the commander employed various teams in combat operations. A red team consisted of two gunships, AH-1G Cobras, with a variety of armament. It was strictly an offensive weapon, readily available to the commander. A white team, consisting of two light observation helicopters armed with 7.62-mm. miniguns, was used to reconnoiter areas where the enemy's situation was unknown and significant contact was not expected. One of these helicopters flew a few feet above the ground or trees to conduct close-in reconnaissance. The other flew at a higher altitude to provide cover and radio relay and to navigate. The higher ship also functioned in a command and control capacity. A pink team was a mixture of red and white, one light observation helicopter and one Cobra. The observation helicopter followed trails, made low passes over the enemy positions, and contoured the terrain in conducting its reconnaissance mission. The gunship flew a circular pattern at a higher altitude in the general vicinity to provide suppressive fire and relay information gathered by the observation helicopter. When outside of artillery range or in areas considered to be extremely dangerous, the pink teams were used in conjunction with a command and control helicopter. If one helicopter was downed by enemy fire, the remaining aircraft provided cover until a reaction force arrived. Pink teams could also adjust artillery fire, although the AH-1G with its twin pods of 2.75-inch rockets was comparable to a 105-mm. howitzer. Pink teams were the most prevalent tactical combination of aircraft in the air cavalry troop.

A blue team was a structured number of UH-1H aircraft transporting the air cavalry troop's aerial rifle (aerorifle) platoon or part of a ground cavalry troop of the cavalry squadron. The blue team normally worked with pink teams. The aerorifle platoon of the air cavalry troop was transported in its organic aircraft in a great variety of roles. When the aerorifle platoon was employed, a rifle company from one of the battalions in the area was designated as the backup, quick reaction force. The air cavalry troops were normally assigned ground and aerial intelligence, security, and economy-of-force missions.

Intelligence missions, oriented on the enemy, included visual reconnaissance of routes, areas, and specific targets, bomb damage assessment, landing zone reconnaissance and selection, target acquisition, prisoner capture (body snatch), and ranger and airborne personnel detector operations. The value of the air cavalry as the eyes of the commander was inestimable. The body snatch was a special operation to capture prisoners or to apprehend suspected enemy personnel. In such an operation, the helicopter demonstrated its flexibility. Using an aircraft and ground force "package" structured to the particular situation, the air cavalry commander pinpointed the target individual by employing scout helicopters and then landed one or more squads of the aerorifle platoons to accomplish the snatch. Scout aircraft screened the area while the Cobras provided cover. The snatch team package normally included a UH-1H command and control ship to direct and co-ordinate the mission. Executed as a quick reaction technique, body snatch operations provided the commander with a rapid means of gaining new intelligence.

Ranger long-range reconnaissance patrols operated in small teams within the division area. The team members were qualified for airborne operations and trained to rappel and use special recovery rigs. They were capable of sustained operations in any type terrain for a period of five to seven days. Air cavalry supported the rangers with UH-1H transport, aeroweapons support, a command and control aircraft, and an immediate reaction force of an aerorifle or airmobile platoon. Techniques to deploy the teams included false insertions, low-level flights, and, on occasion, landing both the aerorifle platoon and the ranger team simultaneously. The aerorifle platoon was subsequently withdrawn, leaving the rangers as a stay-behind patrol. During operations outside the range of tube artillery, the rangers relied heavily on aeroweapons gunships (AH-1G).

Security missions were primarily oriented toward friendly forces to provide them with early warnings and time for maneuver. Security missions included screening operations, first- and last-light reconnaissance of specified areas, and protection for convoys and downed aircraft.

Air cavalry troops often provided surveillance of an extended area around a stationary or moving force. Pink teams maintained radio contact with the ground commander and reported enemy positions, trails, or troop sightings in order that appropriate action could be taken. Pink or red teams were capable of engaging the enemy with their own organic weapons and of adjusting artillery and air strikes to reduce an enemy threat.

When conducting first-light reconnaissance around a unit field location, the pink teams began their flights before daybreak to be on station at first light. En route the team leader contacted the ground unit commander to request artillery advice and to ask whether the ground unit had any particular area of interest. Last-light reconnaissance began an hour and a half before dark in order to be completed by nightfall. When a target was discovered, the team reported to the ground unit responsible for the area and requested clearance to fire. All enemy sightings were reported to the unit in whose area the teams were operating.

The composition of a convoy security force varied with the size of the convoy, the terrain, and the enemy's situation. The scout elements, either one or two armed light observation helicopters, provided fire support, radio relay, rapid artillery adjustment, and command and control. The aeroweapons platoon could provide quick fire support if the convoy were ambushed, and the aerorifle platoon could be quickly brought in to assist. Other helicopters were then used to move the backup reaction force quickly into the ambush area.

When an aircraft was downed within the division area of operations, a pink team was immediately dispatched to locate it. Then an aerorifle or ground cavalry platoon was brought into the area. The pink team screened the area surrounding the aircraft until both the aircraft and security platoon were evacuated. Although platoon personnel were trained to rig aircraft for evacuation, the normal procedure was to bring in a technical inspector and qualified maintenance personnel to prepare the aircraft.

Economy-of-force missions for airmobile cavalry included artillery raids, combat assaults, ambushes, delaying actions, prolonged security for elements constructing fire bases, and base defense reaction force operations.

Artillery raids supported by air cavalry units included both the tube and aerial rocket artillery raids, delivered into areas where the enemy considered himself safe from such fire. During a tube artillery raid, the air cavalry troop reconnoitered the selected landing zone and secured it with an aerorifle platoon before artillery was landed by CH-47 and CH-54 aircraft. Pink teams conducted visual reconnaissance to develop targets of opportunity and were capable of adjusting fire and conducting immediate damage assessment.

The aerorifle platoon was used to exploit significant sightings or to conduct ground damage assessment. In raids by the aerial rocket artillery battalion, the air cavalry units performed similar missions except that no landing zone had to be selected and developed.

Fire base construction missions involved an aerorifle platoon, an engineer team, and a pink team. The aerorifle platoon was inserted (by rappel, if necessary) into the proposed landing zone to provide security for the engineers. After a landing zone had been cleared for one ship, additional engineer equipment was landed to enlarge the area to the required fire base dimensions. Pink teams conducted screening operations around the troop elements; co-ordination was achieved through a command and control aircraft. After a one-ship landing zone was prepared, infantry troops were usually brought in, and the aerorifle platoon could then conduct reconnaissance of likely enemy positions in the vicinity. This platoon was also capable of conducting limited combat assaults and ambushes. When teamed with scout and aeroweapons platoon elements of the air cavalry troop, it constituted a balanced combined arms team.

Although night helicopter assaults were rare in the early operations in Vietnam, the Army did work toward developing effective night techniques. Experience has shown that all missions and roles normally fulfilled by helicopters during daylight hours can be successfully completed in darkness by aircraft equipped with navigation aids and night vision devices. Vietnam proved that helicopters could be used at night to greatly increase U.S. maneuver superiority over the enemy. Most of the night combat assaults were made to reinforce units in contact with the enemy; however, they were also made to gain tactical surprise, position blocking forces, and set up ambushes.

The first night reinforcement of U.S. troops under fire occurred during the firefight following the 1st Squadron, 9th Cavalry, ambush. The landing zone, which could accommodate only five helicopters, was under continuous fire during all landings. The only light available to the pilots was that from machine gun tracer rounds. This firefight also marked the first time aerial rocket artillery was employed at night in close support of friendly positions.

The first night combat assault involving airmobile 105-mm. howitzers occurred on 31 March 1966 as part of Operation LINCOLN by the 1st Cavalry Division (Airmobile). When elements of the 1st Squadron, 9th Cavalry, reinforced by a rifle company, became heavily engaged in the early evening hours, a second rifle company and Battery B, 2d Battalion, 19th Artillery, were brought into a previously unreconnoitered landing zone at 0105 hours. The fire support from the battery contributed significantly to the total of 197 enemy soldiers killed in the engagement.

The first U.S. battalion-size night combat assault took place on 31 October 1966 when the combat elements of the 2d Battalion, 327th Infantry (Airborne), 101st Airborne Division, were lifted into two landing zones near Tuy Hoa by the 48th and 129th Assault Helicopter Companies and the 179th Assault Support Helicopter Company of the 10th Combat Aviation Battalion. Twenty-four UH-1D, six UH-1B, and four CH-47 helicopters were used. The night before, the 10th Combat Aviation Battalion had conducted a deception operation involving a simulated night combat assault with preparatory fire by tactical air, artillery, and gunships and with illumination by flares. The actual operation was executed without preparatory fire and illumination. Pathfinders and security elements were positioned in the landing zones prior to the main assaults. Helicopters flew nap-of-the-earth flight paths to gain further surprise.

The desire to deny the enemy freedom of movement at night led helicopter units to experiment with a variety of lighting systems. The earliest systems were known as the Helicopter Illumination System (Lightning Bug-Firefly) and were characterized by a fixed bank of C-123 landing lights mounted in a gunship. The crew would find and hold the target with the lights while other gunships engaged the enemy. In the Mekong Delta an OV-1C Mohawk was often used as part of the team, locating targets by an infrared device and vectoring the

YO-3A QUIET AIRCRAFT

fall of 1965 and evaluated during combat missions. The results were quite successful; however, all the Buffaloes as well as the Caribous were transferred to the U.S. Air Force in the spring of 1967.

The helicopter and airmobile techniques gave the commander new capabilities; the old time-distance factors and terrain considerations were outmoded. In the airmobile division, the helicopter was not used just as a means of transporting by air—such as troop movement, reinforcement, medical evacuation, and resupply—but was totally integrated into operations by commanders at all levels. The readily available air assets were automatically considered in maneuver plans against the enemy, in intelligence gathering, in fire support, and in logistic operations.

CHAPTER III

IRVING

(2-24 October 1966)

Operation IRVING illustrates a number of innovations which were used throughout Vietnam. These innovations represented important changes in the tactical, technical, and psychological sides of warfare. The helicopter played an enormous part, not only in lifting troops into combat but also as aerial rocket artillery, in the evacuation of casualties, in logistical support, and in the development of new lightweight equipment. IRVING also demonstrates the use of civic action and psychological warfare in counterinsurgency operations. In addition to being outflanked by vertical envelopment, the enemy was attacked by strategic bombers and by U.S. infantrymen invading his underground hiding places.

During October of 1966, allied military forces combined efforts in three closely co-ordinated operations to destroy the enemy in the central and eastern portions of the Republic of Vietnam's Binh Dinh Province and to uproot the Viet Cong's political structure along the province's populated coastal region. In a period of twenty-two days, the 22d ARVN Division, the Republic of Korea Capital Division, and the U.S. 1st Cavalry Division (Airmobile) were to dominate the battlefield to such an extent that the aggressor had only one alternative to fighting: surrender. The enemy not only suffered heavy personnel losses in decisive combat, but many of his vital logistic and support bases were discovered and destroyed. The victory meant that the central coastal portion of Binh Dinh Province and hundreds of thousands of citizens were returned to the control of the South Vietnamese government. The people of the province were freed from Viet Cong terrorism and extortion for the first time in many years, and the groundwork was laid for a better life. The U.S. 1st Cavalry Division's contribution in this campaign to pacify Binh Dinh Province was Operation IRVING.

IRVING began on 2 October 1966; however, the development of the battlefield started many days before. The enemy had been driven out of his bases in the Kim Son and 506 valleys and channeled toward the sea. In Operation THAYER I in September, strong U.S., South Vietnamese, and Korean attacks from all sides uprooted elements of the 610th North Vietnamese Army Division from their mountain sanctuaries, uncovering major medical, arms, supply, and food caches, a regimental hospital, and a large antipersonnel mine and grenade factory. A series of fierce battles forced the enemy into a natural pocket bounded by the Phu Cat Mountains on the south, the coastline on the east, the Nui Mieu Mountains on the north, and National Route 1 on the west. The battle lines for Operation IRVING had been drawn.

The 1st Cavalry Division planned for Operation IRVING in minute detail. The division staff concentrated on intelligence, psychological operations, population control, and civic action projects as well as combat operations. If combat against the enemy was to be successful, the psychological, population control, and civic action aspects had to be effective. In the same pocket with the enemy were some 250,000 civilian residents, plus important rice farming and salt production areas. To avoid noncombatant casualties, population control measures were incorporated into the psychological operations program. Some twelve million leaflets and 150 radio broadcast hours were used during Operation IRVING to help control the civilians. Curfews were established, and at times villagers were requested to stay where they were until more specific instructions were given. Psychological efforts were also geared to appeal to the enemy. For example, substantial rewards were offered for surrendered weapons.

By D-day for Operation IRVING, the Free World Military Assistance forces were in position. Elements of the 1st and 3d Brigades of the 1st Cavalry Division air-assaulted into objectives well inside the IRVING pocket. Simultaneously, the ARVN and Korean elements coordinated attacks in the southern portion of the battle area so that all three schemes of maneuver would complement one another. The 22d ARVN Division launched a ground attack to the northeast with two infantry battalions and two airborne battalions. The Republic of Korea Capital Division attacked northward through the Phu Cat Mountains. On the South China Sea, the ARVN junk fleet and the U.S. Navy sealed escape routes to the sea and provided fire support from the destroyers *Hull* and *Folson* and smaller ships.

The 1st Cavalry Division attacked at 0700 hours on the morning of 2 October. Colonel Archie R. Hyle, commander of the 1st Brigade, deployed the 1st Battalion, 8th Cavalry, to gain objective 506C; the 2d Battalion, 8th Cavalry, to secure objective 506A; and the 1st Battalion, 12th Cavalry, to attack objective 506B. The 3d Brigade commander, Colonel Charles D. Daniel, attacked objective 507 using the 1st and 5th Battalions of the 7th Cavalry. The 1st Squadron, 9th Cavalry, under the control of Major General John Norton, the division commander, was assigned its normal reconnaissance mission over the division's area of interest. Decisive combat with the enemy was to occur shortly after the operation began.

Early on the morning of D-day, elements of the 1st Squadron, 9th Cavalry, were conducting reconnaissance operations in the vicinity of Hoa Hoi and observed seven North Vietnamese Army soldiers in the village. Troop A landed its infantry elements in the village area and supported them with armed helicopters. They soon were engaged against a large enemy force that had fortified the village. When advised of the situation at Hoa Hoi, Colonel Hyle called for the 1st Battalion, 12th Cavalry, already airborne en route to another objective. Lieutenant Colonel James T. Root, commander of the 1st Battalion, issued new orders from his command and control helicopter, and the battalion turned to the rescue.

B Company was the first unit of the 1st Battalion to arrive at Hoa Hoi. Under the direction of Captain Frederick F. Mayer, Company B landed 300 meters east of the village and quickly maneuvered to assault the enemy's fortified positions. Although wounded, Captain Mayer directed the unit's drive toward the well-prepared enemy bunker system. While advancing across an open area, the unit came under extremely heavy fire and was momentarily pinned down. Members of the 2d Platoon, Company B, stood up and advanced through the enemy fire. One squad, spearheaded by Private, First Class, Roy Salagar, breached the heavily booby-trapped perimeter trench, and within minutes the enemy force started withdrawing into the village.

At this time A Company air-assaulted into an area southwest of Hoa Hoi. As the 3d Platoon came in contact with the enemy, they also encountered civilian noncombatants in the battle area. First Lieutenant Donald E. Grigg was deploying his platoon to return fire when several old men, women, and children walked between him and the enemy. He raced 150 meters through concentrated fire, picked up two of the small children, and carried them back to his own lines. The other civilians followed him to safety. Lieutenant Grigg's platoon then closed in on the enemy and forced him to withdraw into the village.

While other elements of the 1st Battalion, 12th Cavalry, were being air-assaulted into the battle area, the battalion held its fire on the village. A psychological operations helicopter circled the village with loudspeakers, directing the civilians to move out of the village and into four specific areas outside the perimeter. North Vietnamese Army soldiers were asked to lay down their weapons. During the moratorium, many civilians and soldiers did as they were directed. After one hour, when it was evident that no one else was coming out of the village, the 1st Battalion, 12th Cavalry, began moving in.

Fierce fighting lasted throughout the day as elements of the U.S. battalion assaulted the fortified village. That evening, General Norton reinforced the 1st Battalion, 12th Cavalry, with Companies A and C of the 1st Battalion, 5th Cavalry. Under the control of Colonel Root, the companies made a night air assault on the beaches east of

Hoa Hoi and moved into the encirclement to help contain the enemy during the hours of darkness. North Vietnamese soldiers tried in vain to shoot their way out. Effective artillery support contributed to the containment effort. Earlier in the day, A Battery, 2d Battalion, 19th Artillery, had been positioned by assault support helicopters to back up the 1st Battalion, 12th Cavalry. During the night 883 105-mm. rounds were fired in the effort to contain the enemy. The battlefield was illuminated by a U.S. Air Force AC-47 flareship, by artillery, and by naval guns from the destroyer *Ullman*. Throughout the night, helicopters provided fire support, brought in supplies, and evacuated casualties.

At dawn, Company C, 1st Battalion, 12th Cavalry, attacked south through the enemy position, while Companies A and B blocked the other side of the village. The enemy defended with great skill; but the strength of the attack, plus the well-co-ordinated combat support, brought the battle of Hoa Hoi to a close. During this 24-hour battle, the 1st Battalion, 12th Cavalry, and supporting units had killed or wounded 233 enemy soldiers, while suffering 3 killed and 29 wounded. In addition, 35 North Vietnamese soldiers were captured, and 15 suspected NVA regulars were detained.

On D-day of the operation a B-52 strike was made on a portion of the Nui Mieu Mountains near objective 506A. The 1st Squadron, 9th Cavalry, conducted a follow-up damage assessment and discovered documents and seven enemy dead, which confirmed the presence of elements of the 2d Viet Cong Regiment. All forces advanced on schedule to reduce the size of the IRVING pocket. The sweep to the sea continued, using helicopter assaults and land movement to destroy the enemy forces. On 4 October a co-ordinated ground attack was made by the 3d Brigade using the 1st and 5th Battalions, 7th Cavalry. The attack was preceded by extensive artillery preparation. Thirty enemy soldiers were killed in the operation. As the sweep operations neared Nuoc Ngot Bay, leaflets and loudspeakers were used to warn civilians that all boats moving on the bay would be sunk. Riot control agents were also used during the operation. The battalions of the 3d Brigade used assault boats brought in by helicopter to sweep the waterways.

On 5 October the 1st Battalion, 12th Cavalry, air-assaulted back to the west into the Soui Ca Valley to exploit a B-52 strike and to surprise enemy units that had escaped the IRVING pocket or had secretly moved into the valley strongholds. In the IRVING battle area, the 1st Cavalry Division continued to search for North Vietnamese units and to uproot the Viet Cong. The 1st Squadron, 9th Cavalry, sighted many small groups of enemy soldiers trying to avoid contact. The cavalrymen fired at them from armed helicopters and often landed infantry elements to engage the enemy. On 9 October, while supporting

CH-54 "FLYING CRANE" DELIVERING BULLDOZER TO FORWARD POSITION

a sweep along the Hung Loc peninsula, the 2d Battalion, 20th Artillery (Aerial Rocket Artillery), fired SS11 missiles at bunkers on the peninsula. The missiles destroyed the bunkers, thus enabling fifty-five Viet Cong to be captured without a fight.

In mid-October, enemy contacts in the coastal region diminished, and the emphasis of the battle shifted back to the valleys in the west. Capitalizing on the information that elements of the 2d Viet Cong Regiment were regrouping in the Kim Son and Soui Ca valleys, the division quickly airlifted several battalions into the area. On 13 October, the 1st Battalion, 5th Cavalry, located the main Viet Cong province headquarters, including official stamps, radios, documents, and typewriters. On 14 and 15 October, in support of the 1st Battalion, Company A of the 8th Engineer Battalion brought in airmobile engineer construction equipment. A CH-54 "flying crane" lifted a grader and a pneumatic roller into the valley. Teams of engineer soldiers called tunnel rats located, explored, and later destroyed extensive tunnel complexes constructed by the enemy. Sweep operations in the valleys turned up additional caches of equipment and supplies.

During the latter part of Operation IRVING an artillery raid was conducted by A Battery, 2d Battalion, 19th Artillery. Four howitzers with crews, 280 rounds of ammunition, and a skeleton fire direction center were airlifted into areas that the enemy had thought were secure to fire on previously selected targets that were beyond the range of other tube artillery. The 280 rounds were fired in less than seventeen minutes, after which the artillery was airlifted back to its base.

By midnight of 24 October the battle was over. The enemy had been unable to cope with the airmobility and versatility of the 1st Cavalry Division (Airmobile). Massive firepower had decimated the enemy's forces, and his long-secure supply bases had been destroyed. While suffering 19 men killed itself, the 1st Cavalry Division had killed 681 enemy soldiers and captured 741. The rapid reaction of U.S. forces allowed the division for the first time to capture more enemy soldiers than it killed. The success of Operation IRVING had a lasting effect on the pacification of Binh Dinh Province.

The major tactical innovation illustrated in Operation IRVING was airmobile combat. An airmobile operation is one in which combat forces and their equipment move about the battlefield in aircraft to engage in ground combat. In such an operation, helicopters not only transport the forces to the battle area, but also enable them to develop the situation and to reinforce, withdraw, and displace combat power during the battle. The purpose of an airmobile assault is to position fresh combat troops on or near their tactical objectives. The tactical unit can fly over obstacles and impassable terrain to land at the strategic point in the battle area.

The successful airmobile assaults in Operation IRVING and those conducted by other units in Vietnam were the result of detailed planning by the participating ground units, the aviation support elements, and the combat support and combat service support units. The overall commander of an airmobile task force is the commander of the ground unit making the assault. The aviation commander directs the helicopter support units and advises the task force commander on all aviation matters.

Airmobile operations in Vietnam were planned in an inverse sequence, similar to airborne operations. First, the ground tactical plan was prepared. It was the basic airmobile operation plan. In this plan the commander of the assault unit presented his scheme of maneuver and plan for fire support in the objective area. Assault objectives were chosen that insured the accomplishment of the mission. Landing zones were then carefully selected to support the ground tactical plan. A fire support plan was developed concurrently in order to be closely co-ordinated and integrated with the scheme of maneuver.

The next step in the sequence was the development of a landing plan. It insured the arrival of the various elements of combat power at the times and locations required. The landing plan included the sequence, time, and place for landing troops, equipment, and supplies.

An air movement plan was then prepared, which was based on the previous plans. Its purpose was to schedule the movement of troops, equipment, and supplies by air from pickup to landing. Details such as flight speeds, altitudes, formations, and routes were specified.

Finally, a loading plan was developed. It insured the timely arrival of units at pickup zones and the loading of troops, equipment, and supplies on the correct aircraft at the proper time.

Often, because of rapidly changing tactical situations, the airmobile planning sequence was abbreviated. All elements of the planning were considered, but in a shorter form. The actions of Colonel Root of the 1st Battalion, 12th Cavalry, in Operation IRVING provide an excellent example. Plans were prepared for an airmobile assault by the 1st Battalion on objective 506B. However, when directed at the last minute to assault the village of Hoa Hoi, Colonel Root prepared and assigned new orders while en route by air to the new objective. Sound training and complete standing operating procedures for the ground and aviation units contributed to the quick development of airmobile plans and orders.

Radio communications and prearranged visual signals, colored smoke, and flares were the primary means of communication during airmobile assaults.

Fire support was extremely important during these operations and included artillery, naval gunfire, armed helicopters, tactical aircraft, strategic bombers, and mortars. During a specific operation the task force may have been supported by any or all of these means. All available fire support was controlled by the airmobile task force command group from its command and control helicopter. Preparatory fire on and around the landing zone was usually brief but intense and continuous, with no pause in the firing from the various sources. Fire was shifted from the landing zone only seconds before the first flight of helicopters touched down. The firing was diverted to selected locations to protect the assault force, and then redirected to support the expansion of the objective area. Smoke was often used by artillery or by a specifically equipped helicopter to mask the movement of the assault force.

Division commanders in Vietnam concluded that airmobile assaults greatly increased the speed and flexibility of their operations, extended their area of influence, and provided them with the means to concentrate forces quickly and to move them after accomplishing the mission.

In World War II and in the Korean War, where combat ranges were normally greater than in Vietnam, gunnery errors seldom resulted in friendly casualties. Any round that cleared friendly lines was usually safe. In Vietnam, however, about 50 percent of all artillery missions were fired very close to friendly positions or into an area virtually surrounded by converging friendly forces. An error could harm U.S. or allied troops or civilians living in the areas of operations. The senior officer in charge of each area of operation was specifically charged with the safety of his troops and of the local population. His fire support co-ordinator worked out the details required to insure this safety. He used such devices as no-fire lines, fire and fire support co-ordination lines, and clearances with the lowest level of the Republic of Vietnam government (usually the district) that had U.S. advisers. Fire support co-ordinators maintained a map marked to show specified-strike zones and no-fire zones, all based on the rules of engagement drawn up jointly by U.S. and Vietnamese high commands. They were applicable to all allied forces and were meant to protect the lives and property of friendly forces and civilians and to avoid the violation of operational and international boundaries. The rules were specific. They covered each general type of operation, such as cordon and search, reconnaissance in force, a waterway denial operation, and defense of a base camp. They also governed the establishment of zones. No-fire zones were those in which persons loyal to the Republic of Vietnam government lived. The rules provided for the different curfew hours which each province chief specified for all Vietnamese civilians in urban centers, along main supply routes, in New Life hamlets, and in the woods and fields. Presumably, all persons who were not in a no-fire zone obeying curfew restrictions were suspect.

Naturally, the rules did not limit the right of a unit to defend itself, and a unit attacked could take necessary aggressive action against the enemy with any means available. As Major General Harris W. Hollis later stated:

> The clearest test of the hostility of a target was the receipt of fire from it—prima facie evidence, as it were. In such cases our units or aircraft could return fire as a matter of self-preservation, but only to the degree necessary to deal with the threat. No overkill airstrike could be called down on a Viet Cong sniper without proper prior clearance. I am convinced that this restraint by each responsible commander played a key role in minimizing civilian casualties.

The most serious problem created by clearance requirements was the loss of indirect fire responsiveness and surprise. As a rule, clearances added approximately three minutes' delay for each agency required to take action on the request. Agencies within a unit caused the least delay and complications.

To reduce the time lost in firing missions, nonpopulated areas were frequently cleared in advance of operations and for night intelligence and interdiction fire. Commanders were expected to establish appropriate liaison with local government agencies and with Free

World forces to provide quick request channels and to mark specified-strike zones whenever possible.

With the tremendous increase in the use of aircraft in the Republic of Vietnam came the need to assign responsibilities for their safety from indirect ground fire. Operational responsibility for the air advisory agencies was usually given to the major field artillery headquarters in the area. The agencies were generally located with a battalion operations section. Aircraft entering the area of an air advisory agency usually radioed in for clearance. They were given the locations of all fire or of safe routes to travel. The agency notified aircraft in its area about new artillery missions by calls over its network. The responsibility for all fire above 5,000 feet was passed by the air advisory agencies to the U.S. Air Force.

An important innovation in the Vietnam War was the integration of strategic air power into the ground combat plan. Similar use of heavy bombers in Korea was on a much more limited scale. The Strategic Air Command, with its B-52 bombers flying at extremely high altitudes, out of sight and out of hearing of the unsuspecting enemy, delivered devastating blows against fortified positions. Two B-52 strikes were used in Operation IRVING.

Ground commanders used the B-52's against targets of high tactical value. Enemy troop concentrations in base areas were common targets. When a B-52 target was identified, a request was passed through command channels to a joint Army-Air Force targeting committee. If the request was approved, the target was included in the bombing schedule and the requesting unit was notified. The tactical commander could then complete his plans for using the B-52 strike to its best advantage on the ground. The follow-up operation after the bombing raid, depending on the nature of the target, ranged from a small patrol reconnoitering the area to a large-scale sweep operation involving a battalion-size unit or larger. Artillery was often used following a B-52 strike to hit enemy personnel moving back into the target area.

The tactical mobility furnished by the helicopter and the communications available to the ground commander were effectively used to capitalize on B-52 strikes. While the dust and smoke from the bombs were still in the air, the heliborne assault could begin, taking maximum advantage of the shock and confusion among the enemy troops.

One of the major artillery innovations of the Vietnam War was aerial rocket artillery, commonly called ARA, and later, aerial field artillery. The fire support potential of the helicopter had been appreciated for some time. Gunships, in the form of UH-1 helicopters armed with various combinations of machine guns, rockets, and grenade launchers, had been effectively used throughout the conflict.

Theoretically, however, the gunships provided light fire support rather than the artillery type. Aerial rocket artillery, on the other hand, was organized and employed as artillery. In the words of Lieutenant Colonel Nelson A. Mahone, Jr., commander of the 1st Cavalry Division's 2d Battalion, 20th Artillery (ARA), "We consider ourselves a breed apart, and our success tends to support this." Aerial rocket artillery fire was requested through artillery channels and was usually controlled by an artillery forward observer. ARA was particularly effective in support of airmobile forces beyond the range of the division's ground artillery. Moreover, ARA fulfilled the need for a highly responsive and discriminating means of fire support for the infantry during its most vulnerable phase of an air assault, namely, just after its arrival on the landing zone. Aerial rocket artillery helicopters circling overhead watched over the landing zone and movement of the troops. If necessary, they immediately responded to fire requests by firing directly on the target.

Although ARA was frequently used beyond the range of cannon artillery, it also augmented this fire. ARA was assigned the normal tactical missions of conventional artillery. Normally, however, it was used in general support with control retained by division artillery because of ARA's range and flexibility.

The main armament of the ARA consisted of the M3 2.75-inch folding-fin rocket system mounted on UH-1 helicopters, and later on the Cobra version. In addition, the ARA was capable of using the SS11 antitank wire guided missiles. SS11 fire was extremely valuable against point targets, such as bunkers located on hillsides and other enemy fortifications. Medium and heavy artillery in Vietnam was normally located in semipermanent base camps or fire bases to provide support within the tactical area of operations. Continuous fire, or the threat of it, from these weapons caused the enemy to move his base camps and supply caches out of range. The artillery raid was used against these outlying enemy installations by moving to a position in range of the target, firing on the enemy, and then returning to the artillery's base. Medium and heavy self-propelled weapons were particularly well suited for raids, although light and medium artillery lifted by helicopters could be used. In fact, the airmobile divisions achieved excellent results with helicopter-borne 105-mm. howitzers used in this fashion, and they developed expedient methods of clearing jungle artillery bases. This technique was used effectively in Operation IRVING.

In October 1969, the 101st Airborne Division (Airmobile) developed the radar raid in order to extend the influence of its artillery. This type of raid was conducted by frequently moving AN/PPS-4 or AN/PPS-5 radars with security forces to dominant terrain features outside fire bases. These forces could then provide surveillance along routes of infiltration previously masked by terrain. By conducting raids within existing artillery ranges, discovered targets could be rapidly engaged.

During Operation IRVING, Company C, 2d Battalion, 8th Cavalry, discovered a tunnel complex in the Nui Mieu Mountains. The complex included five vertical shafts, thirty to fifty feet deep, with horizontal tunnels connecting them. After searching the tunnels, a squad of engineers from the 8th Engineer Battalion destroyed the complex with demolitions.

A significant feature of the war in Vietnam was the widespread use of tunnels and other underground facilities by the enemy. Tunnels were a major factor in the enemy's ability to survive bombing attacks, to appear and disappear at will, and to operate an efficient logistic system under primitive conditions. By the end of 1970, 4,800 tunnels had been discovered. Most of the discoveries were made during sweep operations by Free World military forces. Tunnel complexes were also located through local informers and by means of dogs trained to find underground facilities. An electronic tunnel detector and a seismic detector were tested with limited success. Several techniques have been developed to force the enemy to evacuate tunnels. Tunnel rat teams were formed by many infantry and engineer units to clear and explore tunnels. An exploration kit consisting of headlamps, communications equipment, and a pistol assisted the team. A Tunnel Explorer Locator System was developed to map the tunnel and to monitor the progress of the tunnel rat as he moved through the tunnel. Proven chemical techniques were the use of smoke to locate tunnel openings and a riot control type of tear gas, known as CS, to drive enemy personnel from underground.

After tunnels were cleared and searched, they were destroyed to prevent their further use by the enemy. Methods developed to keep the tunnels from being used again included placing riot control agents in the tunnel, sealing the entrance with explosives, using demolitions to destroy the tunnels, pumping acetyline into the tunnel and igniting the gas by explosives, and using construction equipment to crush the tunnels.

The first use of riot control agents in Vietnam was on 23 December 1964 when CS grenades were air-dropped as part of an attempt to rescue U.S. prisoners being held at a location in An Xuyen Province. In this operation no contact was actually made with the enemy. In February 1965, General Westmoreland informed the senior advisers of the four corps tactical zones that U.S. policy permitted the use of riot control munitions in self-defense. Kits containing protective masks and CS grenades were issued to each subsector advisory team for self-defense. These kits were not intended for offensive use by U.S. troops.

MEMBERS OF AN ENGINEER TUNNEL RAT TEAM *explore Viet Cong tunnel.*

In March 1965, New York *Times* correspondent Peter Arnett described the use of riot control agents by ARVN forces. His report generated much controversy in both the American and foreign press and led to an examination, by both U.S. military and political agencies, of the pros and cons of the use of CS in Vietnam. An independent action by the commander of the 2d Battalion, 7th Marine Regiment, on 5 September 1965 significantly influenced subsequent policy on the use of CS in Vietnam. The 2d Battalion encountered an enemy force entrenched in a series of tunnels, bunkers, and "spider" holes. Since there was information that women and children were also present, CS was used to help clear the complex. As a result, 400 persons were removed without serious injury to noncombatants. However, on 7 September 1965, all senior U.S. commanders were reminded that "MACV policy clearly prohibits the operational use of riot control agents."

Later the same month, the Military Assistance Command, Vietnam (MACV), decided that the military usefulness of CS warranted a request to higher authority for permission to use it in the upcoming Iron Triangle operation. The request was forwarded to Secretary of Defense Robert S. McNamara, who granted permission for CS to be used in the Iron Triangle operation only. In the following weeks, a much-liberalized policy on the use of CS was developed, and on 3 November 1965 the Joint Chiefs of Staff notified General Westmoreland that he was authorized to use CS and CN (another tear gas) at his discretion to support military operations in South Vietnam. This authority was further delegated to the major commanders.

MACV Directive 525-11, dated 24 July 1967, concerned the use of riot control agents in tactical operations. Using these agents in situations where noncombatants were involved was deemed particularly appropriate. The U.S. senior advisers to the four ARVN corps were empowered to authorize the use of CS by U.S. forces in support of the South Vietnamese Army. U.S. advisers at all levels were to encourage their counterparts in the Vietnamese armed forces to use CS and CN whenever such use offered an over-all tactical advantage. The use of riot control agents in situations involving civil demonstrations, riots, and similar disturbances was specifically prohibited without prior approval by the commander of the Military Assistance Command, Vietnam. Riot control agents were treated as normal components of the combat power available to the commander.

The early use of CS was limited by the shortage of standard munitions. The only munitions available at first in operational quantities were the M7 and M25 grenades. Many other ground and air munitions were being developed and later were tested and used in Vietnam.

One of the first uses for M7 CS grenades was to flush caves, tunnels, and other underground fortifications. The 1st Cavalry Division

(Airmobile) effectively used CS grenades during Operation MASHER-WHITE WING, which took place in a highly populated area. CS grenades when used on suspected enemy areas enabled 1st Cavalry troops to determine whether the occupants were civilians in hiding or armed Viet Cong. On another occasion, forty-three Viet Cong were pursued into a cave. All forty-three were driven out again, however, when CS hand grenades were thrown into the cave. The only casualty occurred when one Viet Cong refused to surrender.

RIOT HAND GRENADE, CS1, M25A2

The burning-type CS grenade, along with HC smoke grenades, was also used in conjunction with the M106 Riot Control Agent Dispenser, dubbed Mity Mite, a portable blower. This system was capable of forcing the Viet Cong and North Vietnamese Army out of unsophisticated tunnel complexes, as well as helping to locate hidden entrances and air vents. The Mity Mite system could not drive personnel from the more complex, multilevel tunnel systems, many of which contained airlocks. However, bulk CS was widely used in tunnel denial operations, in which bags of CS were exploded throughout the tunnels. The 1st Infantry Division's experience indicated that the tear gas remained effective for five to six months if the tunnel was sealed. The efficiency of powdered CS in restricting the enemy's use of fortifications and the difficulty of destroying the numerous bunkers and other fortified structures by conventional explosives led to the development of many techniques for dispensing CS in these enemy defenses.

The 1st Cavalry Division (Airmobile) termed their expedient munition the Bunker Use Restriction Bomb (BURB). The BURB consisted of a cardboard container for a 2.75-inch rocket warhead, two nonelectric blasting caps, approximately twenty-five seconds of time fuze, and a fuze igniter. The device was filled with CS and taped shut. The blasting caps provided sufficient explosive force to rupture the container and to spread the CS49. Other units developed their own expedient CS munitions for contaminating fortifications.

The acceptance of CS as a valuable aid in combat operations led to the development of several weapons systems. These included the E8 riot control launcher; the XM15 and XM165 air-delivered tactical

CS clusters; the 40-mm. CS cartridge for the M79 grenade launcher; the 4.2-inch mortar CS round; the BLU52 chemical bomb (Air Force); and the XM27 grenade dispenser. The E8 chemical dispenser was used effectively by the 2d Battalion, 5th Marine Regiment, during Operation HUE CITY between 3 and 15 February 1968. The action during this period was characterized by close, intense house-to-house combat. Engagements with the enemy were usually at distances from 20 to 150 meters, with maximum distances of 300 meters. The use of air and artillery forces was limited by weather conditions and by the closeness of the enemy to friendly troops. The tactical situation required almost continual assaults on fortified buildings and some bunkers. The use of the E8 CS dispenser was credited with neutralizing the enemy's firepower during the assaults.

The greatest amount of CS employed in Vietnam was bulk CS1 or CS2 dispensed to restrict the enemy's use of terrain. Contamination of large areas or of terrain not accessible to friendly ground forces was normally carried out by air-delivered 55-gallon drums that contained eighty pounds of CS. The drums were dropped from CH-47 helicopters using locally fabricated racks, which allowed the unloading of thirty drums on the target. The major targets for these drops were known or suspected base camps, rest areas, and infiltration routes.

Air-delivered, burning-type munitions also produced good results as evidenced by the use of thirty E158 air-delivered CS clusters in support of South Vietnamese Rangers on 3 February 1968. The Rangers were heavily engaged by a large Viet Cong force deployed in a factory complex in the Cholon area of Saigon. After several attacks by the Rangers had been repulsed, the CS munitions were dropped into the area by helicopter. The Ranger assault which followed the CS drop was successful.

The use of riot control agents by U.S. and allied forces in Vietnam cannot be likened to the gas warfare of previous wars. Whereas mustard and chlorine gas often resulted in permanent injury and death, CS and CN produced only temporary irritating or disabling physiological effects. Their use saved the lives of many allied soldiers, civilians, and enemy soldiers.

Because of the extensive use of helicopters in the Republic of Vietnam, landing zones had to be rapidly constructed in heavily forested areas, like those surrounding the Kim Son and Soui Ca valleys. The engineers in Vietnam were thus challenged to reduce the landing-zone construction time, in order to meet the needs of the quickly shifting tactical situation. Landing zone requirements ranged from the hasty construction of a helicopter pad, from which to provide emergency resupply or medical evacuation, to the development of large landing zones, able to handle sufficient aircraft to support battalion or brigade operations.

Experience gained by engineer units in Vietnam led to the development of landing zone construction kits that contained the necessary tools and demolitions to prepare a landing zone for one aircraft. If the engineer team could be landed near the new construction site, they would rappel from the helicopter or climb down rope ladders. When sufficient area had been cleared, air-portable construction equipment or additional tools and demolitions were lifted in to expand the new landing zone.

The "combat trap" was developed after experimentation. In a joint Army and Air Force effort, an M121 10,000-pound bomb was parachuted from a fixed-wing aircraft or helicopter over the desired landing zone site and detonated at a height that would clear away the dense foliage but not create a crater in the earth. After the combat trap had finished its job, a construction party and equipment were taken by helicopter to the new landing zone to expand it to the desired size.

The key to the success of airmobile operations often was the ability of the engineer battalion to construct landing sites for helicopters and fixed-wing aircraft quickly. To support the airmobile division adequately, air-portable construction equipment was developed for the division's engineer battalion. Engineer equipment that could be moved into the forward areas by helicopter included roadgraders, bulldozers, scoop loaders, scrapers, and cranes, each of which was sectioned and lifted into the objective area in two loads, and then assembled for operation. Backhoes, small bulldozers, dump trucks, and compaction equipment could be transported in one helicopter lift.

Throughout Operation IRVING the 8th Engineer Battalion used airmobile construction equipment to clear and expand landing zones and artillery positions and to construct defensive positions. On 14 October, a bulldozer, a grader, and a roller were sectioned and airlifted to the command post of the 1st Brigade, 1st Cavalry Division, to expand the existing landing zone and to construct an aircraft refueling area.

The cry of "Medic! Medic!" has been heard in all wars involving the United States, and the company aidman is still the first link in the chain of medical support. In Vietnam the aidmen had a new lifesaving tool, the medical evacuation helicopter, better known as Dust-off. Because of the bravery and devotion to duty of these helicopter pilots and crews, many lives were saved. Often Dust-off choppers landed under heavy enemy fire to pick up wounded soldiers or hovered dangerously above the battlefield as an injured man was hoisted up to the helicopter. The seriously wounded were taken directly from the field to a hospital, often bypassing the battalion aid station and the clearing station. This rapid means of evacuation saved many lives and greatly improved the soldiers' morale. Each soldier

Dust-off Helicopter Hoists Wounded Man From Battlefield

knew that if he were wounded he would be picked up immediately by Dust-off.

Although the helicopter was a great help to the men in Vietnam, it required considerably more engineer support than the Army originally expected. As the commanding general of the engineers in Vietnam, Major General David S. Parker, noted in his debriefing report, "In addition to advanced landing zones, built primarily by division engineers through a number of ingenious techniques, there have been extensive requirements for revetments, parking areas, maintenance hangars, and paved working areas for POL, ammunition, and resupply operations. The construction has increased effectiveness through added protection and improved maintenance."

Parked aircraft were prime targets for the enemy and, as such, were subjected to many damaging small arms, mortar, and rocket attacks. Therefore, the protection of organic aircraft was a major concern to all commanders. Engineers were charged with providing lightweight, portable, and easily erected revetments for all helicopters without decreasing the helicopter's reaction time. Construction materials included airfield landing mats, plywood, corrugated steel, and soil.

The T17 nylon membrane was an important development for engineer support of airmobile operations. The membrane was designed as a moisture barrier and dust cover for landing zones and strips. It was also used successfully as the surface for unloading aprons and parking areas, thereby greatly reducing construction time. It was not a cure-all, however, since it added no bearing strength to the soil. The blast from helicopters often created large dust clouds, which increased aircraft collisions and maintenance difficulties. The T17 membrane was one way of reducing dust, but peneprime, a commercial composition of low-penetration grade asphalt and a solvent blend of kerosene and naphtha, was the best dust control agent tried in Vietnam. During Operation IRVING, the 8th Engineer Battalion used some 38,600 gallons of peneprime on helicopter pads, refueling areas, and airfield turnarounds.

Operation IRVING was an excellent example of recent changes in the tactics of war. The airmobile division, with Vietnamese and Korean assistance, demonstrated its flexibility and power as it pursued and destroyed a large enemy force in a populated countryside. The helicopter became an integral part in maneuver plans, division artillery, medical evacuation, and the transport of heavy equipment. The enemy was hit with everything from strategic bombers to tunnel rats, within the confines of special rules of engagement. Psychological operations and population control were also included in the tactical plan.

CHAPTER IV

Loc Ninh (October-November 1967)

The 1st Infantry Division's operations around Loc Ninh in October and November 1967 illustrates many of the tactical and materiel innovations used by the infantry commander in Vietnam. New formations and techniques were employed to find the enemy. Dogs, starlight scopes, and anti-intrusion devices helped the units to avoid being surprised. Carefully planned defensive measures for small unit tactical perimeters were developed by the division, and new, lighter weapons with increased firepower made the foot soldier more effective. Other new techniques increased the support provided by artillery, by air, and by Army aviation.

Events leading up to the battle of Loc Ninh included the engagement of the 1st Battalion, 18th Infantry, with elements of the 271st Viet Cong Regiment at Da Yeu, fifty-five kilometers south of the Loc Ninh airstrip. This firefight clearly demonstrates fire support in Vietnam. It also illustrates the use of scout dogs and the cloverleaf formation, a conventional reconnaissance technique adapted to the infantry battalion's movement toward contact with the enemy.

The battle was fought in dense scrub jungle, where observation was limited to ten feet. The 1st Battalion, 18th Infantry, was commanded by Lieutenant Colonel Richard E. Cavazos and had been operating in the vicinity of Da Yeu for seven days, searching for elements of the 9th Viet Cong Division. On the morning of 11 October Companies B and C and the battalion tactical command post moved out of the position that the battalion had occupied without contact during the night. Company B, commanded by Captain Watson G. Caudill, led, followed by the tactical command group and Company C, which was commanded by Major William M. Mann, Jr. The mortars were left in the night defensive position with Company D. (Company A was in Di An on a rear area security mission.) The mission was to search for an enemy base camp believed to be two kilometers north.

The point squad of Company B was accompanied by a scout dog, which immediately gave the alert as the company cleared the perimeter. In response to the dog's alert, the column proceeded in a cloverleaf formation in order to provide maximum security. No enemy was sighted; however, the point squad reported hearing movement to its front and the dog continued to give the alert. After covering 1,800 meters, Captain Caudill directed his front platoon leader, 1st Lieutenant George P. Johnson, to deploy his troops in line and direct small arms fire into the forward area. The fire was immediately returned from a range of thirty meters, whereupon Colonel Cavazos ordered Captain Caudill to withdraw his platoons through each other and move into the defensive perimeter being formed by Company C. Meanwhile, Captain Robert Lichtenberger, Company B's forward observer, had called in artillery. As the 1st and 2d Platoons withdrew through the 3d Platoon, he guided the artillery fire back with them until it was falling only 100 meters from the 3d Platoon's positions and well inside the initial point of contact. Second Lieutenant Ralph D. McCall had selected an excellent position for his 3d Platoon to cover the withdrawal of the remainder of the company. His squads were linked with Company C. Because the heavy enemy fire was ineffective, Colonel Cavazos directed the 3d Platoon to maintain its position rather than pull back into the perimeter.

By 1015, forty-five minutes after the initial contact, the first of nine tactical air sorties was attacking 400 meters in front of Lieutenant McCall's 3d Platoon and just north of the east-west fire co-ordination line that had been established by Colonel Cavazos. Simultaneously, the artillery was striking in the area between the 3d Platoon and the fire co-ordination line.

At 1020, a helicopter light fire team entered the battalion net for instructions. After noting the smoke that identified the front and flank elements, the fire team leader began to search the battalion's west (left) flank. He had been directed to run from south to north, to work his fire up to the artillery impact area, and to break west to avoid conflict with the fighters which were striking from east to west and breaking north. The enemy reacted immediately to the fire team's first run. Seventy-five Viet Cong, who had been hiding on the left flank, assaulted the 3d Platoon. They were cut down by the U.S. infantrymen firing from their positions behind trees and anthills. The charge ended as abruptly as it started. The 3d Platoon was moved back into the perimeter as the artillery was shifted even closer to the battalion's position. After another hour, in which artillery, tactical air forces, and helicopter fire teams continued to work the area, enemy firing ceased and the battalion (minus) moved forward. Twenty-one bodies were found in the enemy position. The 1st Battalion, 18th Infantry, had one man killed and four wounded (all from the 3d Platoon of Company B) during the Viet Cong assault.

During the three-hour contact, the battalion was never decisively engaged. The final assault into the enemy position was not started

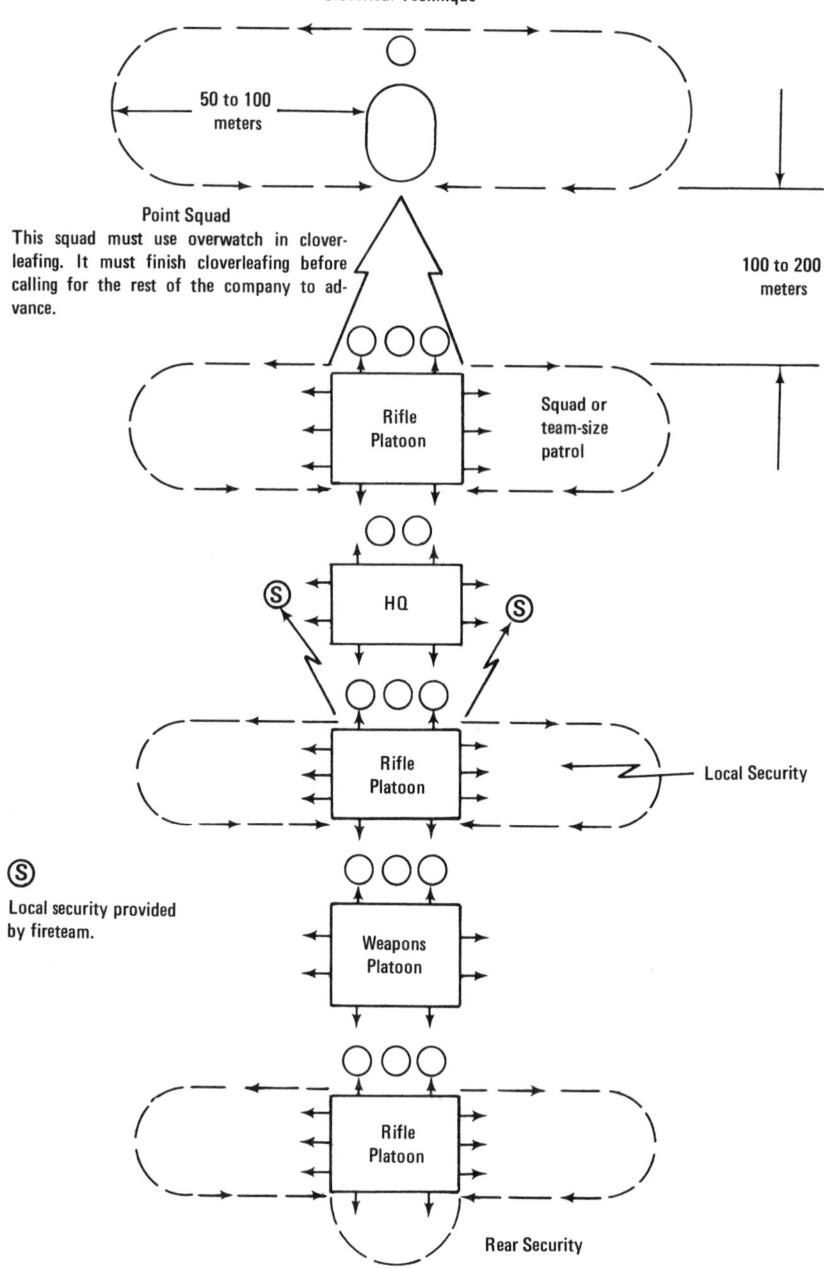

Diagram 1. Rifle company cloverleafs, advancing toward contact.

until enemy firing had ceased. The combined firepower of tactical fighters. armed helicopters, and artillery was directed simultaneously on the enemy position, which had been detected from an airborne scent picked up by a scout dog.

The cloverleaf formation, named for the trace of the patrols that emanated from the main column, was used habitually by the 1st Infantry Division when contact with the enemy was imminent. It provided for a deliberate search of the flanks of a column and for an "overwatch" technique used by the point squad. (*Diagram 1*) In the overwatch, one element moved while another element occupied a position from which it could fire immediately in support of the advancing point men. Using this formation, the enemy position was discovered before the entire unit became engaged.

Assigning the helicopter fire team to cover the battalion's flank was another new technique in the Vietnam War. Although successful commanders in all wars have been concerned about the security of their units' flanks, the war in Vietnam demanded even greater attention. This new emphasis resulted from the relative independence of small unit operations, from the nature of the terrain, and from the enemy's ability to hide his formations close to U.S. forces.

Scout dogs also proved to be a valuable innovation. A scout dog team consisted of one dog and one handler, trained to work together and inseparable for operational purposes. Scout dogs were German shepherds and normally worked on a leash. They were trained to respond to airborne scents by signaling their handlers when they picked up a foreign presence. Scout dogs could locate trip wires, mines, fortifications, tunnels, and storage areas. Under ideal conditions, they could detect groups of people several hundred meters away; however, fatigue, adverse weather conditions, and dense vegetation affected their performance. In addition to the scout dog was the tracker dog. The tracker, a Labrador retriever, was part of a team consisting of the dog, his handler, and four men trained in visual tracking techniques. The dog, working on a 25-foot leash, followed a ground scent over terrain where the soldier-trackers were unable to pick up visible signs. The first combat tracker teams used in Vietnam were trained by the British in Malaya. Now the Military Police School at Fort Gordon, Georgia, has the facilities for tracker training.

The battle of Da Yeu was an unqualified defeat for the North Vietnamese Army; it was indicative of the outcome of subsequent contacts in the vicinity of Loc Ninh. Loc Ninh is a district town 13 kilometers from the Cambodian border and 100 kilometers north of Saigon. The town was slated as a target by the 9th Viet Cong Division for late October. The timing coincided with the inauguration of President Nguyen Van Thieu; the seizure of a district capital by the enemy could have had substantial political impact.

Scout Dog Leads Patrol Searching for Viet Cong

During the weeks that preceded the battle, the headquarters of the 9th Viet Cong Division left War Zone D for the border area north of Loc Ninh. The division headquarters moved with the 273d Viet Cong Regiment and approached the border areas where the 272d Regiment had already assembled. The 271st Regiment, the third of the division's three regiments, moved into the Long Nguyen secret zone, fifty kilometers south of Loc Ninh. A captured enemy document indicated that this move was made to facilitate the logistic support of the 271st Regiment. However, after several contacts with elements of the U.S. 1st Infantry Division, including the battle of Da Yeu, the 271st Regiment withdrew from the area in late October. The regiment had sustained over 400 killed in action during its brief tenure in the Long Nguyen secret zone, and it was probably too weak to be committed at Loc Ninh. The 165th Viet Cong Regiment was subsequently directed to provide additional men to the 9th Division in order to fill in the ranks.

The enemy's scheme of maneuver directed the 272d and 273d Viet Cong Regiments to converge on Loc Ninh. The 272d Regiment was to approach from the northeast and the 273d was to approach from the west. The operation began at 0100 hours on 29 October, when the

CIDG Compound and Loc Ninh Airstrip *with A Battery, 6th Battalion, 15th Artillery, position in the foreground.*

273d Regiment attacked the district headquarters and the Civilian Irregular Defense Group (CIDG) and Special Forces camp at the Loc Ninh airfield. The 273d Regiment pressed the attack until 0535 when it was forced to withdraw. Although it had briefly penetrated the CIDG compound, it left 147 Viet Cong bodies on the battlefield.

In reaction to the attack, Major General John H. Hay, Jr., commander of the 1st Infantry Division, alerted four battalions and their supporting artillery. General Hay's plan was to deploy the battalions in a rough square around Loc Ninh. A study of the terrain and the pattern of enemy activity in the area revealed the most probable enemy routes of approach and withdrawal. The battalions were to set up night defensive positions at the corners of the square and to block the enemy's withdrawal. Artillery was to be placed in each of the night defensive positions to insure mutual support as well as support for the maneuver battalions' operations. The locations of these positions—temporary fire bases—on routes essential to the enemy would challenge him to attack; and as he massed for the assault, fire from supporting artillery, tactical fighters, and helicopter fire teams would be directed on his exposed formations. In addition to the units along the routes of withdrawal, the plan included bolstering the defenses of Loc Ninh with a small force of infantry and artillery.

At 0630 on 29 October the 1st Battalion, 18th Infantry, commanded by Colonel Cavazos, made an air assault into the southwestern corner of the square, four kilometers west of the Loc Ninh airstrip. Elements of the 2d Battalion, 28th Infantry, commanded by Major Louis C. Menetrey, and two batteries of artillery were moved to the airstrip. The 1st Battalion, 26th Infantry, and the 1st Battalion, 28th Infantry, were moved to Quan Loi, from where they could be committed as the situation developed.

By 1215 the 1st Battalion, 18th Infantry, had made contact with a Viet Cong company. This engagement, the first of six major firefights that comprised the battle of Loc Ninh, resulted in another twenty-four enemy soldiers killed. At 1215 the following day the 1st Battalion, 18th Infantry, again made contact, and the 273d Viet Cong Regiment lost eighty-three men. At 0055 hours on 31 October, the 272d Viet Cong Regiment made its bid from the northeast for the Loc Ninh district headquarters and the CIDG compound, now reinforced with elements of the 2d Battalion, 28th Infantry, and Battery A, 6th Battalion, 15th Artillery. The 272d Regiment withdrew at 0915, leaving 110 bodies and 68 weapons around the airstrip. To block the withdrawal of the 272d Regiment, the 1st Battalion, 28th Infantry, commanded by Lieutenant Colonel James F. Cochran, III, conducted an air assault three kilometers southeast of the airstrip. Although the battalion made sporadic contact for several days following the assault, it was unable to re-engage the enemy significantly. While the 1st Battalion, 28th Infantry, blocked the southwest withdrawal route of the 272d Regiment, the 1st Battalion, 18th Infantry, searched the area west of the airstrip.

In the early morning hours of 2 November, the night defensive position of the 1st Battalion, 18th Infantry, became the battlefield for the fourth major engagement of the battle for Loc Ninh. The 1st Division's after action report described the conflict as follows:

> 2 Nov—The 1/18th Infantry NDP [night defensive position] came under heavy mortar attack commencing at 0030H and lasting for 20 minutes. The mortar positions were reported by ambush patrols, one being directly south of the NDP and one being located to the southwest. About 5 minutes later, Company A ambush patrol reported movement coming from the south. The VC were in the rubber guiding north along a road which led into the NDP. The ambush patrol blew its claymores and returned to the NDP. One VC was KIA [killed in action] attempting to follow the ambush patrol inside the NDP.
>
> To the east, Company D's ambush patrol reported heavy movement and the patrol was ordered to return to the perimeter. Company C ambush patrol located north of the NDP also reported movement. The patrol blew its claymores and returned to the NDP. The VC attacked the NDP from three sides, northeast, east and south. Artillery and mortar defensive concentrations served to blunt the assault. Two VC armed with flamethrowers were killed before their weapons could be fired.
>
> As the artillery was brought in close to the NDP from one direction, the VC fire would diminish and build up from another direction.
>
> When LFT's [helicopter light fire teams] arrived on station they were directed to expend on the main attacking force to the south. The gunships as well as the FAC [forward air controller] and the AO [aerial observer] received heavy machinegun fire from three locations to the south. Fire from 12

heavy machineguns was identified. Airstrikes eliminated the positions. The artillery battery inside the NDP was directed to be prepared to fire antipersonnel rounds. The guns were readied but their use was not required.

Contact was broken at 0415H. U.S. casualties were 1 KHA [killed hostile action] and 8 WHA [wounded hostile action]. There were 198 VC KIA and 22 KBA [killed by air] by body count in the immediate vicinity of the NDP. For the next five days patrols found additional VC bodies bringing the final body count to 263 VC KIA (BC) [body count] and 6 POW's [prisoners of war]. There were 18 individual weapons, 10 crew served weapons, and 3 flamethrowers captured. The flamethrowers were Soviet Model. . . . The unit was identified as the 273d VC Regiment. There were 50 sorties of tactical air flown in support of the contact.

November 2d was the fifth day of the battle for Loc Ninh. The enemy had attacked Loc Ninh twice and had been defeated both times. The U.S. battalions blocking his retreat were deployed on the southeast and southwest withdrawal routes. Intelligence indicated that it was now time to close the escape routes to the north. The 2d Battalion, 12th Infantry (attached to the division for this operation), and the 1st Battalion, 26th Infantry, were assigned the mission. The 2d Battalion, 12th Infantry, commanded by Lieutenant Colonel Raphael D. Tice, air-assaulted seven kilometers northeast of Loc Ninh; the 1st Battalion, 26th Infantry, commanded by Lieutenant Colonel Arthur D. Stigall, landed six kilometers northwest. The landings were unopposed, and both battalions established night defensive positions in the vicinity of their landing zones. The four corners of the square were now occupied by U.S. battalions, each supported by carefully positioned artillery batteries. At 2340 eight Viet Cong walked into the 2d Battalion, 12th Infantry, position, half of them carrying flashlights. Four of the enemy were killed and four were captured. They were members of the 272d Viet Cong Regiment. The U.S. battalion's position was attacked at 0220. When the fight was over, twenty-eight enemy bodies were left around the perimeter.

The final engagement of the battle for Loc Ninh occurred on 7 November, when two companies of the 1st Battalion, 26th Infantry, engaged the 3d Battalion of the 272d Viet Cong Regiment. The 1st Battalion, 26th Infantry, had been airlifted out of the area on 6 November after having spent four days northwest of the airstrip without a significant contact. The battalion air-assaulted into an area two kilometers west of the 2d Battalion, 12th Infantry—roughly eight kilometers northeast of Loc Ninh. The day after the air assault, Companies C and D and Colonel Stigall's command group engaged the 3d Battalion, 272d Regiment. Artillery, armed helicopters, and twenty-seven air strikes supported the U.S. troops. Ninety-three enemy soldiers were killed, including twenty-seven by air strikes. The battle of Loc Ninh was over.

Of the six major engagements that comprised the battle of Loc

SERGEANT AND RIFLEMAN ENGAGE ENEMY WITH M16 RIFLES

Ninh, two were fought in temporary night defensive positions. The use of night defensive positions in Vietnam was brought about by the lack of conventional front lines, the inclination of the enemy to fight at night, and the need for the tactical units to protect themselves. The principles of defense were unchanged from earlier wars, but their application to night defensive positions included a number of new techniques. The most widespread of the innovations was the increased emphasis on defensive operations throughout the Army—an army that has been and will probably continue to be oriented to the attack, rather than to the defense. Companies and battalions in previous wars had been integrated into the defensive plans of larger units to a far greater extent than was possible on the battlefields of Vietnam. The independence of these units required a new emphasis on all aspects of defensive operations by company and battalion commanders. For example, in the past a battalion commander in a defensive position on the forward edge of a conventional battle area could expect the brigade headquarters to deploy a security force in front of his position. He could also expect additional forces in the form of a general outpost to be deployed forward of the brigade's outposts. The battlefield in Vietnam, however, was not adaptable to these traditional arrangements, and the extensive security echelons that characterized the night defensive positions in Vietnam were the sole responsibility of the battalion or company commanders who organized the positions.

The principles of defense were professionally applied to the night defensive positions at Loc Ninh. In the 2 November attack on Colonel Cavazos' night position, one American was killed and eight were wounded. The enemy body count was 263. Among the primary factors that contributed to these and other similarly impressive results was the position that had been standardized in the 1st Infantry Division.

During SHENANDOAH II the VC attacked a night defensive position on five separate occasions: 6 October, 11 October, 31 October, 2 November and 3 November. The US KHA [killed hostile action] totaled seven. The VC KIA was 509 by body count. One of the major reasons why the friendly casualties were so low was the 1st Infantry Division fighting position. This fighting position has become standardized throughout the division and provides each soldier with adequate overhead cover, overhead clearance, and protective berm to the front with firing apertures at a 45 degree angle, a berm to the sides, adequate near protection and thorough camouflage. The fighting position is completed during the first day in a new NDP, before the soldier is allowed to sleep.

A second factor that contributed significantly to the effectiveness of U.S. units in Vietnam was new weapons. The M16, the standard rifle, took eight years to progress from the drawing board to combat in the U.S. Army. It was designed by the Armalite Division of Fairchild Aircraft Corporation in 1957 and sent to Vietnam with the 173d Airborne Brigade in 1965. Initially the rifle was the target of some criticism because sometimes it would unexpectedly stop firing. Technical modifications were therefore made on the weapon. These improvements, along with a significant effort to train the troops in its care and cleaning, removed any doubts about the reliability of the M16 in combat. The M16 muzzle velocity was higher than that of its predecessor, the M14, which significantly increased the destructiveness of the bullet at close range. The relatively light weight of M16 ammunition (half the weight of the 7.62-mm. NATO round) allowed the soldier to carry a larger basic load and reduced the frequency of resupply. The M16 was dependable, easy to maintain, and capable of being fired as either a semiautomatic or automatic weapon. It proved particularly valuable in the jungle where visibility was poor, targets were fleeting, and contact was normally at short range.

The history of the M79 grenade launcher is longer than that of the M16, but it too first met the test of combat in Vietnam. Development of the 40-mm. M79 began in 1952; however, it was not until 1961 that a substantial quantity was available for issue to units. With the M79, units in Vietnam could engage the enemy with a fragmentation round beyond normal hand grenade range. High explosive was the

CLAYMORE MINE, ARMED AND READY TO FIRE

most commonly used round, although other types of ammunition were available. The M79 was useful in conducting ambushes and counterambushes; destroying point targets, such as machine gun positions; providing illumination; and marking targets for air strikes. The weapon was a universal favorite with U.S. troops in all units from infantry to quartermaster.

These small arms and support weapons were coupled with night surveillance devices to give U.S. units a significant advantage over the enemy in night operations. The night surveillance devices most commonly used in Vietnam were the searchlight, sniperscope, starlight scope, and radar. Among these, the innovation was the starlight scope. This device weighs only six pounds and, when mounted on an M16 rifle or M60 machine gun, can fire effectively at night out to 300 meters. The principle of the starlight scope is amplification of existing light. In situations where no natural light was available for the starlight scopes, artificial illumination from searchlights, flares, and other light sources was used. In addition to the individual model, larger crew-served starlight scopes were also manufactured.

Other new equipment related to night defensive positions was also introduced in Vietnam. Anti-intrusion devices, such as various types of sensors, supplemented the security echelons at night. Kits including fortification material and mortars that could not be carried cross-country were delivered and removed from unit night positions by helicopter. The claymore mine became a part of virtually every night position in Vietnam.

The claymore mine, which was developed by the U.S. Army before the war, was introduced into combat in Vietnam. The mine weighs 3.5 pounds and has a casualty area the height of a man out to fifty meters. Most importantly, it can be aimed to cover a specific area. In fixed positions claymore mines were used in depth, with overlapping kill zones. In ambush positions the ratio of one mine to two men was not uncommon. The claymore mine was particularly effective to open an ambush because the extensive, instantaneous kill zone that it generated did not disclose the location of the ambush patrol. The ingenuity and speed with which claymores were positioned became a matter of professional pride with infantrymen in Vietnam. The mine's effectiveness has insured its retention in the U.S. Army's arsenal.

Many of the problems encountered were unique among the recent experiences of artillerymen, and the solutions to some of these problems were necessarily innovative. The classic artillery roles remained unchanged, but how the units were used often differed from previous wars. Because of the large areas that needed protection and the enemy's surprise tactics of ambush, raid, and attack by fire, artillery units were required to respond almost instantly to calls for defensive fire. Any U.S. or allied installation without this support was inviting attack by the North Vietnamese Army and Viet Cong. Such instant response required spreading the artillery thin and resulted in the inability to mass fire, as was done in World War II and Korea. Large amounts of firepower were delivered, but instead of firing a few rounds from many weapons—as was the case in more traditional warfare—many rounds were fired from the few tubes within range of the target.

The "speed shift" of the 155-mm. howitzer was an example of the ingenuity of artillery innovations in Vietnam. During the first few months of Vietnam combat, 1st Lieutenant Nathaniel W. Foster of the 8th Battalion, 6th Artillery, 1st Infantry Division, developed a simple, effective device to allow rapid shifting of the 155-mm. towed howitzer. The old method involved lowering the weapon down off its firing jack, picking up the trails, and pointing the piece by hand in the new direction of fire. At best, this action was a time-consuming procedure involving considerable effort for at least eight men. Under less-than-ideal conditions, particularly in mud, such a shift was accomplished only with tremendous difficulty. This problem considerably hampered the ability of the 155-mm. towed units to meet the 360-degree firing requirement that existed in Vietnam.

The solution to the problem was a locally fabricated "pedestal" positioned under the howitzer carriage at the balance point. In use, the howitzer was lowered until its weight rested on the pedestal. It was then possible to pick up the trails and swing the howitzer in any direction in seconds. The average crew strength was six. Because of its effectiveness, the speed shift pedestal came into general use within the 8th Battalion, 6th Artillery, in the spring of 1966. In Operation BIRMINGHAM, Battery B, with Lieutenant Foster as its executive officer, fired over 7,200 rounds during nineteen days and performed innumerable shifts using the pedestal. One gun was shifted thirty-three times in one critical nineteen-hour period.

A new response to the need for heavy artillery was the 175-mm. gun, which was used in combat for the first time in Vietnam. The gun was a corps-level weapon and could permanently cover large tactical areas of operations, thus freeing the smaller caliber division artillery units to support the maneuver units. Furthermore, the 175-mm. gun when teamed with the reliable eight-inch howitzer was even more effective.

Central tactical control of all field artillery units was exercised in Vietnam to insure the most efficient use of available firepower. However, an artillery mission was generally carried out at the lowest possible level, usually battery or platoon. Brigadier General Willis D. Crittenberger, Jr., Commanding General, I Field Force Artillery, described the situation as follows:

> This war, at least from the Force Artillery point of view, is largely a battery commander's war—the junior officer must really be on his toes, thinking ahead, making his wants known in advance, for his battalion staff is miles away. In addition, the various fire support bases are established in several locations, so one can cover another. The battery commander then must be self-reliant. Vietnam is a great training ground for the leaders of the future.

Unique problems that arose from the unconventional nature of the war in Vietnam were, of course, not limited to artillery. Tactical control measures were also a major difficulty. One geographical area in Vietnam might well contain American tactical units; third country forces; Vietnamese regular tactical units; American Special Forces detachments; and irregular units, such as Regional Forces, Popular Forces, and People's Self-Defense forces. Clear boundaries were needed between these units to avoid the tragic consequences of friendly fire landing on allied positions. At the same time, unity of command was required to insure that friendly units, regardless of make-up or nationality, were reinforced in the shortest possible time when necessary.

In the spring of 1967, the II Field Force commander, Major General Frederick C. Weyand, introduced a new solution to the tactical control problem. In co-ordination with the Vietnamese III Corps

General Westmoreland and General Hay

commander, he divided the zone into "tactical areas of interest" and assigned them to subordinate commanders. These tactical areas of interest were normally extensions of the tactical area of responsibility. In the tactical areas of interest, commanders were not charged with primary tactical responsibility, and they were not expected to conduct operations on a continuing basis. The commander to whom a tactical area of interest was assigned, however, had to know the location, activities, and operations of all forces and installations in his area and, through mutual co-operation and co-ordination, to achieve the maximum effect from the combined friendly forces and firepower available. This arrangement worked extremely well. Not only did it provide local unity of command, but it served to increase the confidence and aggressiveness of the Vietnamese Army commanders who shared areas of operation with U.S. tactical elements. The Vietnamese commanders knew that their U.S. counterparts would provide resources and firepower when they needed them.

Brigadier General Henry J. Muller, Jr., served in Vietnam on both sides of this arrangement. As assistant division commander of the 101st Airborne Division, he participated directly in providing support, primarily helicopters and firepower, to the commanders of the 1st ARVN Division. Later, he became the deputy senior adviser to the Vietnamese I Corps commander, Lieutenant General Lam. In this capacity he co-ordinated support to I Corps from the 101st Airborne Division and other U.S. units. He attributed the remarkable progress of the Vietnamese divisions in the I Corps area primarily to the close association between the Vietnamese units and the U.S. tactical elements in their common operational area.

The key innovation of Loc Ninh was the exploitation of the tremendous tactical mobility available to the 1st Infantry Division. When the battle started with the attack on the airstrip, there were no regular U.S. Army units around Loc Ninh. Immediately the 1st Battalion, 18th Infantry, most of the 2d Battalion, 28th Infantry, and two batteries of artillery were committed. Two more battalions were standing by twenty kilometers south at Quan Loi, ready to be flown in by helicopter on a few minutes' notice as the situation developed. On 2 November, the fifth day of the battle, two additional battalions stationed 100 kilometers to the south were flown in and attached to the 1st Infantry Division. This ability to react with entire battalions and their supporting artillery on short notice and the concomitant ability to withhold the battalions until the enemy has committed himself were major innovations of the war.

Such unprecedented mobility coupled with the firepower available to 1st Division commanders laid the foundation for the victory at Loc Ninh. Time-tested principles, new weapons, starlight scopes and other surveillance devices, claymore mines, responsive artillery, and innovative tactical control measures all contributed. Finally, the individual soldier, well trained and well led, was the decisive factor. In the words of General Westmoreland at the conclusion of the battles around Loc Ninh: "This operation is one of the most significant and important that has been conducted in Vietnam, and I am delighted with the tremendous performance of your division. So far as I can see, you have just made one mistake, and that is you made it look too easy."

CHAPTER V

REMAGEN and MONTANA MAULER (March-April 1969)

Military operations in rough or mountainous terrain usually call for infantry; however, the 1st Brigade, 5th Infantry Division (Mechanized), conducted successful operations in the highlands of Vietnam with an armored-mechanized force. Several materiel innovations made this success possible: the exclusive use of cargo helicopters to establish a line of communications, new aerial resupply techniques to assist the helicopters in providing logistical support, and the use of the armored vehicle launched bridge (AVLB) to maintain ground mobility within the task force. Finally, the organization of the brigade itself was an innovation that gave it great flexibility and power.

The 1st Brigade, 5th Infantry Division (Mechanized), a unique and versatile organization, was the last major U.S. tactical unit to arrive in Vietnam. It included the 3d Squadron, 5th Cavalry; the 1st Battalion, 11th Infantry (Light); the 1st Battalion, 61st Infantry (Mechanized); the 1st Battalion, 77th Armor; and the 5th Battalion, 4th Artillery (155-mm. Self-propelled). Shortly after arriving in Vietnam the brigade was placed under the operational control of the 3d Marine Division. The brigade's commander received most of his combat and combat service support from the division. The brigade often conducted combined operations with South Vietnamese forces in the near-trackless terrain adjacent to the demilitarized zone and the Laotian border. In April of 1969, Colonel James M. Gibson conducted a dual operation by splitting his brigade: an armored infantry task force operated on the Khe Sanh plateau, and the rest of his force engaged in Operation MONTANA MAULER in the central demilitarized zone.

In March 1969, intelligence reports indicated that the North Vietnamese once again were moving across the Laotian border in the direction of the A Shau Valley. Air reconnaissance had revealed an extension of Route 926, which the Viet Cong were building from the old Route 92 on the Ho Chi Minh Trail, across the lower end of the Khe Sanh plateau in the direction of the A Shau Valley. Long-range patrols had reported hearing trucks and tracked vehicles moving along this new road.

Because of these reports, the 3d Marine Division deployed one reinforced regiment to prevent the enemy from using this route and to search out possible North Vietnamese Army base areas in the northern extension of the A Shau Valley. At the same time, the XXIV U.S. Corps commander sent an armored task force to the Khe Sanh plateau to open up Route 9 to Khe Sanh, cut Route 926, and protect the west flank of the Marine regiment. This armored force was composed of elements of the 1st Brigade, 5th Infantry Division (Mechanized). It was given the code name of Task Force REMAGEN and consisted of two mechanized infantry companies; a tank company; a self-propelled, 105-mm. artillery battery; a reinforced armored engineer platoon; a platoon of 40-mm. antiaircraft "dusters"; and a battalion headquarters element. Initially, command and control of the task force was provided by the 1st Battalion, 77th Armor. Later, this unit was replaced by the 1st Battalion, 61st Infantry (Mechanized), and the task force was enlarged. A troop of ARVN cavalry was among the units reinforcing the task force. Each battalion headquarters brought its organic scout and mortar platoons, its combat trains of tracked maintenance vehicles, and most of its supply section. At the height of the operation, there were over a hundred tracked vehicles in the task force and no wheeled vehicles.

In March 1969, the last secure position on Route 9 was at a bend in the road called Ca Lu. From this point, the road wound upward through a valley for about thirty miles until it reached a high plateau. The ruins of the ancient town of Khe Sanh sat along a stream in the middle of this plateau. The infamous airstrip lay about a mile north of the town.

There were several narrow defiles and one unfordable mountain stream along the road from Ca Lu to Khe Sanh. An armored vehicle launched bridge was needed to span the stream. However, since there were no forces available to secure this span and the adjacent defiles, the bridge had to be retrieved after the last vehicle in the armored column had crossed. This meant that there would be no land line of communication behind Task Force REMAGEN. The armored task force had to be supplied completely by air during the entire operation.

For forty-seven days, Task Force REMAGEN ranged up and down the Laotian border. It cut the Viet Cong Route 926, it defeated several attacks by elements of two North Vietnamese Army regiments, and it took a heavy toll of enemy casualties. It also captured numerous enemy weapons, documents, and equipment. During this time, the men of the task force consumed over 56,000 meals, used over 59,000 gallons of gasoline and diesel fuel, and fired over 10,000 rounds of artillery ammunition. The maintenance sections of the task force installed 12 engines, 18 sets of tracks, and 7 transmissions and performed numerous other maintenance chores under field conditions. All of this material and equipment was brought to the task force in the field by Army CH-47 (Chinook) or Marine CH-46 helicopters. This feat involved a considerable logistic effort, representing about fifteen sorties by the supply helicopters every day for forty-seven days. In addition to the CH-47 and CH-46 helicopters, brigade UH-1 helicopters were used to deliver mail, meals, and spare parts.

Mechanized infantry played a key role in the success of the operation. It provided one of the two command and control headquarters, bore the brunt of the fighting, took the greatest number of casualties, and inflicted a resounding defeat upon the enemy in every engagement. In this instance, the mechanized rifle companies served in their traditional role, reinforced with the tank company. However, these rifle companies operated in a wild and rugged area over thirty miles from the nearest friendly installation. Once again, they demonstrated their flexibility and proved that no terrain was inaccessible to them.

From their sanctuaries across the Laotian border, the North Vietnamese launched a number of attacks against the night positions of the task force. A typical night attack occurred on 25 April, beginning with an extensive mortar barrage at 0330 hours. An estimated battalion from the 304th North Vietnamese Army Division was attempting to overrun and destroy the night defensive position of the 2d Troop, 7th ARVN Cavalry. Team ARVN, as the unit was designated, was under the operational control of the 1st Battalion, 61st Infantry (Mechanized). The heavy mortar barrage was followed by a determined ground attack using rocket propelled grenades, small arms, automatic weapons, flamethrowers, and satchel charges. Unable to penetrate the position, the enemy quit the field at 0600 leaving behind 33 dead North Vietnamese soldiers, several weapons, and 300 prepared satchel charges.

Three days later the enemy tried again. The commander of Company A, 1st Battalion, 61st Infantry (Mechanized), had prepared his defenses well. The company was alerted by the men at a listening post, who sprang an ambush on the enemy soldiers as they were moving into position. Again, the enemy attack was supported by fire from rocket propelled grenades, mortars, small arms, and automatic weapons. Throwing satchel charges and using flame devices, the enemy troops charged from the southwest but were unable to penetrate the perimeter. Before dawn they again withdrew and disappeared into the night. This time 34 of their soldiers were killed, small arms and automatic weapons littered the battlefield, and 500 satchel charges lay undetonated.

At 1100 hours, Company C, 1st Battalion, 11th Infantry, was air-assaulted into the area to help re-engage the enemy. At the same time the remainder of the 1st Battalion, 11th Infantry (Light), was functioning as part of Operation MONTANA MAULER, being conducted far to the northeast also by the 1st Infantry Brigade. Enemy contact by this element was recorded in the brigade's after action report.

> Two ground troops of the 3d Squadron, 5th Cavalry, were sent into an area in which an NVA Regiment was suspected to be located. Being small enough to invite an attack by an enemy regiment, yet strong enough to be able to defend itself until reinforcements could arrive, the cavalry was able to draw the enemy into a fight. Once contact was gained the cavalry was able to develop the situation so that additional forces could be intelligently committed to the battle in an attempt to close with and destroy the enemy.

The 1st Battalion, 11th Infantry, was being used as an airmobile reserve, prepared to reinforce the cavalry. When this battalion was later committed, a U.S. Marine Corps rifle company was attached to it. Thus a most unusual combination resulted: REMAGEN, a U.S.-ARVN armored-mechanized infantry force, without a single wheeled vehicle and no land resupply route; and MONTANA MAULER, with light infantry in airmobile reserve. Both of these forces contained Marine Corps units, and the brigade reported to the 3d Marine Division. Lieutenant General William B. Rosson, Commanding General, I Field Force, Vietnam, said of such operations:

> I am persuaded that the mixture of Marine Corps and Army forces within III MAF [Marine Amphibious Force] is a desirable and productive arrangement. Indeed, of things learned during my several assignments in Vietnam, I accord top billing to the realization that when Marine Corps and Army units are teamed together, as in Provisional Corps Vietnam, their capabilities combine to produce a force possessing greater power and effectiveness than would be the case if the same units operated separately. Rich are the gains in cross infusion of ideas and experiences. Equally rich are rewards achieved by shifting of assets belonging to one service to support operations by the other when such action promotes the common good, e.g., helicopters, artillery, tanks, amtracks.

Task Force REMAGEN displayed this shifting of assets from one service to support another, as Marine resupply helicopters supported the task force and Marine artillery fired in support of it.

Several measures were taken to accomplish the aerial resupply. A forward supply element was established at Vandergrift Combat Base, where supplies and repair parts were assembled for shipment by helicopter to Task Force REMAGEN. All types of class-I supplies, such as sundry packs, B rations, and C rations, were also stockpiled. Petroleum, oil, and lubricant supplies were ordered from brigade stocks to meet demands as they occurred. Over 75,000 gallons of fuel were delivered to the maneuver units in 500-gallon rubber drums. The transfer of fuel from the 500-gallon rubber drums to the armored vehicles of the task force sometimes posed a problem. Wherever possible, the force of gravity was used; however, a modified M113 bilge pump was

UH-1 Helicopter Makes Delivery

500-GALLON COLLAPSIBLE DRUMS FILLED WITH FUEL

designed and constructed by the task force maintenance section. This pump greatly reduced the restrictions on the refueling of the vehicles. The brigade's supply officer made arrangements with the Marine Logistics Support Unit for the supply of munitions. As the after action report on Task Force REMAGEN stated:

> Overall, Task Force Remagen received from Vandergrift over 200 aerial lifts representing over 1° million pounds plus an additional 50,000 pounds of hot meals, mail and spare parts flown in on brigade UH-1's. A UH-1 was a daily necessity for retail distribution of parts, mail and meals from the combat trains area to the users.

During this period, Operation MONTANA MAULER was also being resupplied by air with an average of 12.7 short tons a day. Certain aerial resupply procedures and techniques were developed due to the jungle environment and monsoon weather in the Republic of Vietnam.

Natural sources of water were sparse in the area where forces were committed to Operation MONTANA MAULER. As in many other operations in Vietnam, water had to be transported to the troops by helicopter. There were several ways to carry the water. The water can usually issued by the government could be used; however, once the water was consumed, the troops either had to wait for the helicopter to return to carry away the empty cans or they had to destroy them. They were too bulky and heavy for the rifleman to carry over the broken and rough terrain. Although plastic water containers could be collapsed when empty and therefore were much easier to carry on the backs of troops, they too were a nuisance. They were frequently lost or damaged in the jungle.

The troops of the 1st Brigade, 5th Infantry Division (Mechanized), developed a third method to supply water to the rifle companies in the field. The empty shell casings provided by the 5th Battalion, 4th Artillery (155-mm. Self-propelled), were cleaned and filled with water and transported to the troops in large numbers. Once the shell casings were empty, they were either buried or otherwise discarded. In this way, troops were not burdened by the containers, and they could not be used by the enemy.

A lightweight collapsible container, nicknamed "lug-a-lug," was also used. This container, as in the case of the five-gallon metal water container, could not be air-dropped from any appreciable height above the jungle canopy. Therefore, the unit on the ground still had to clear a landing zone. A newer container was developed consisting of several plastic inserts protected by a crushable cardboard covering. It could withstand a free fall of up to 300 feet and thus often eliminated the need to clear a landing zone. This three-gallon container proved to be very useful.

Before the commitment of Task Force REMAGEN, other innovations had been developed in Vietnam to improve aerial resupply techniques. Early in 1967, the A-22 cargo sling was employed. This device decreased the number of man-hours spent in preparing resupply items for aerial delivery, reduced the amount of handling, and allowed more sorties to be flown in a given period of time. Also, because of the insulation of the cargo bag, there was less spoilage of food. In another effort to improve aerial resupply, artillery ammunition was packed ahead of time for aerial delivery loads during periods when the demand was light, in order to allow a continuous flow during periods of heavy demand.

Inclement weather, a frequent deterrent to aerial operations in Vietnam, was combated somewhat by using ground controlled approach radar in landing zones for aerial resupply under instrument flight conditions. The procedure was developed initially at Camp Evans, a major logistic base in South Vietnam. Resupply helicopters were guided by means of a radioed vector from Da Nang and Hue-Phu Bai airfields to areas above the overcast where visual flight was possible and then directed to Camp Evans. Ground controlled approach radar would then guide the helicopter as it approached touchdown. This method was also used successfully with helicopters carrying external (sling) loads. During the month of February 1968, the 228th Combat Support Helicopter Company flew over 700 hours in instrument weather conditions. Included in that figure were over twenty missions with sling loads. Several hundred instrument approaches were made without a single mishap. The system established during Operation DELAWARE in April 1968 to provide instrument approach into the A Shau Valley is a good example of this radar technique. Over twenty aircraft could be controlled or monitored simultaneously by radar to and from the valley.

A simple expedient was developed by the infantryman to provide visual contact between air and ground elements during darkness. The M79 grenade launcher was broken open as when loading the weapon, and a light source was inserted in the breech. This practice provided a highly reliable directional signaling and marking device, which could be seen clearly by the pilot or aircraft crew but not by other persons on the ground. The operator merely pointed the light as though aiming at a target.

To reach the Laotian border area and the Khe Sanh plateau, Task Force REMAGEN had to cross over old Route 9 from Ca Lu to the border. Engineer troops had been attached to assist in this job. Company A, 7th Engineer Battalion, provided a reinforced engineer platoon, and four bulldozers were made available by the 14th Engineer Battalion and the Marine 11th Engineer Battalion. The armored vehicle launched bridges in the task force served a dual purpose. The power and traction of the vehicle made it an excellent tank retriever, when not being used in its primary role. The task force had two of these vehicles. The AVLB can launch its eighteen-meter bridge without exposing the crew to enemy fire. The launcher can then pick up the bridge on the far bank and continue along in support of the assault forces. During the operation, thirteen bypasses were constructed around destroyed bridges, the AVLB's were launched six times to span washouts and bridge abutments, and the entire road was swept for mines. Several enemy antitank mines were detected and destroyed along the route. The engineer effort was greatly simplified by using only track-laying vehicles during the operation. Wheeled vehicles of any type were prohibited.

Part of the mission of Task Force REMAGEN required the pioneering of a new trail along the Cambodian border from Route 9 south to Route 926. In heavy growth, land navigation sometimes became a problem due to limited visibility. One device used to solve this problem was a magnetic pilot compass mounted in the armored personnel carrier to maintain the approximate proper magnetic azimuth for the force.

The success of Task Force REMAGEN was described by Lieutenant Colonel Carmelo P. Milia, Commanding Officer, 1st Battalion, 77th Armor, in these words:

> The mission was a natural for an armored task force. The scouts reconnoitered; mech infantry moved rapidly to secure the high ground; armored

ARMORED VEHICLE LAUNCHED BRIDGE

engineers pioneered a road; armored artillery and mortars provided continuous fire protection. When the preliminary work was completed, the tanks thrust deep into the Khe Sanh plateau reaching the Laotian border one day after crossing the LD at Calu [*sic*].

The 1st Brigade, 5th Infantry, presented a good example of the innovative nature of the war in Vietnam. The rugged, unpopulated territory, the enemy's nearness to its supply bases, and the large area of operation required fast-moving, independent task forces capable of aerial resupply and reinforcement.

CHAPTER VI

Coronado X (January-February 1968)

Just before the 1968 lunar new year (*Tet*) truce, the 2d Brigade of the 9th Infantry Division launched riverine operations in the marshlands of the Mekong Delta under the code name Coronado X. An Army-Navy mobile riverine force searched out the Viet Cong's main force and local battalions in a combination of riverine, search and destroy, patrolling, and interdiction operations. When the Viet Cong violated the temporary truce by attacking eight major cities in the delta, the mission of the mobile riverine force was refocused toward crushing the *Tet* offensive.

In Operation Coronado X new equipment and techniques had to be developed for tactical mobility and fire support in the delta area, where conventional techniques were only marginally effective. The terrain was, for the most part, inundated. Swamps, rice paddies, irrigation ditches, rivers, and canals, while inhibiting the mobility of regular U.S. forces, had been used to advantage by the enemy. The mobility achieved by the riverine and airmobile forces changed this situation.

The Mekong Delta had been a target of the Viet Cong for many years. This important rice-producing area covers about one-fourth of Vietnam but contains approximately one-half of the country's population. Most of the people live in villages built along the banks of the 2,500 miles of interconnecting waterways. Since the limited network of roads often becomes impassable in the rainy season, the Viet Cong used the waterways as their chief routes for transporting men and equipment. While the helicopter allowed the allied commander to move forces with little regard to terrain, the water lines of communication were important to military operations and to the civilian economy. The Mobile Riverine Force was organized to prevent the enemy from using the waterways and to make the river system safe for the residents of the delta.

A land base had to be created in the delta area to support the Mobile Riverine Force, because there was little land available that was suitable for bases, airfields, and artillery firing positions. At a point about forty-five miles south of Saigon the base was built, using

USS Benewah, Afloat Base for Mobile Riverine Force, *with armored troop carriers and monitors tied alongside.*

dredges to pump soil from the My Tho River into adjacent rice paddies. The camp, christened "Dong Tam," covered about 600 acres and provided housing and logistic facilities for the 9th Infantry Division headquarters, division support elements, and the Mobile Riverine Force. The base also had a harbor large enough to handle an LST (landing ship, tank).

In addition to the land base, mobile floating bases, consisting of naval barracks ships and watercraft, were used. The Navy elements of the Mobile Riverine Force were organized to provide an afloat base as well as combat support and combat service support to the ground forces. A river support squadron supplied barracks, repair, salvage, and supply ships. A river assault squadron contained armored troop carriers, command and communication boats, monitors (the tank of the riverine force), and assault support patrol boats. Each river assault squadron was equipped to transport and support an infantry battalion conducting combat operations in the delta.

During Coronado X, Colonel Bert A. David, commander of the 2d Brigade, controlled the 3d Battalion, 47th Infantry; the 3d Battalion, 60th Infantry; and 3d Battalion, 34th Artillery. Captain

Robert S. Salzer, U.S. Navy, commanded the Navy elements supporting the 2d Brigade.

The Mobile Riverine Force had been conducting searches in the rice paddies of western Dinh Tuong Province when the Viet Cong launched a devastating attack against the city of My Tho. At 1730 hours on 31 January, the 2d Brigade was ordered to go to the relief of the city. When the order was received, elements of the 2d Brigade were located near Fire Support Bases ALABAMA, FLORIDA, and GEORGIA. Company B, 3d Battalion, 47th Infantry, moved to My Tho by helicopter, while other units of the 3d Battalions, 47th and 60th Infantry, boarded their armored troop carriers and moved south to the Mekong River. During night movement through narrow, uncharted, and shoal-ridden streams, the riverine force came under several attacks from small arms, automatic weapons, and rocket fire. The attacks were beaten off as barge-mounted artillery from the 3d Battalion, 34th Artillery, fired beehive rounds directly at both sides of the river. Accurate fire from the Navy monitors and other watercraft raked the banks. The two battalions and supporting artillery reached the Mekong River and joined up with the afloat base at 0220 hours on 1 February. After a short period of resupply the Army and Navy elements steamed for My Tho. Company B, 3d Battalion, 47th Infantry, which had air-assaulted into My Tho earlier, secured the beach landing sites for the battalion. The battalion beached at 1515 hours with three companies abreast and immediately began to advance north through the west side of My Tho. Automatic weapon and mortar fire from the Navy monitors and from assault support patrol boats and the barge-mounted artillery were in support. The 3d Battalion, 60th Infantry, beached to the west of the 3d Battalion, 47th Infantry, and also attacked to the north. The 47th Infantry's 3d Battalion became involved in fierce street fighting with elements of the 261st, 263d, and 514th Viet Cong Battalions. Lieutenant Colonel Ivan C. Bland moved his companies slowly and effectively, house to house and street by street. Additional artillery, air strikes, and helicopter gunships were called in to support the attacks. At the end of the day the two battalions made physical contact with the enemy and prepared night defensive positions. The 47th's 3d Battalion had killed fifty-eight Viet Cong and captured four, while losing two U.S. soldiers. The 60th's 3d Battalion killed twenty-six Viet Cong and suffered none killed in action. By 2100 hours most of the fighting had ceased, and the enemy had begun to withdraw. The next morning, 2 February, the two battalions encircled My Tho in a combined operation with Vietnamese units to sever the enemy's routes of escape. Only light resistance was encountered as the battalions located several enemy soldiers killed in the previous day's battle. The number of Viet Cong killed by the 2d Brigade rose to 106. For their heroic action in the battle of My

Tho, ten soldiers of the 2d Brigade were awarded Silver Stars on the spot by Major General George G. O'Connor, 9th Infantry Division commander.

The Mobile Riverine Force was not allowed to rest on its laurels, however, as much work had yet to be done. The Viet Cong were retreating to the northwest. Intelligence indicated that the area around Cai Lay was the likely location for the Viet Cong reorganization. At 1200 hours on 2 February, the 2d Brigade loaded back onto its armored troop carriers. Company A, 3d Battalion, 47th Infantry, was transported to Dong Tam and air-assaulted to Cai Lay. The riverine force moved west to the Ba Rai River, where it turned north toward Cai Lay. The 2d Brigade conducted search operations and blocked major rivers in order to frustrate enemy attempts to reorganize. Large food caches were discovered during search operations, but contact with the enemy was limited.

The next day, word was received that the Viet Cong were threatening to take over the city of Vinh Long, which had been hard hit. On 4 February, three Viet Cong battalions were still located south and west of the city. The 60th Infantry's 3d Battalion was moved by rivercraft to a suitable helicopter pickup zone near Cai Lay and, from there, was delivered by air assault to landing zones southwest of Vinh Long. The 3d Battalion of the 47th Infantry boarded armored troop carriers near Cai Lay and moved to beaches on the Long Ho River, southwest of Vinh Long. The battalion landed unopposed and established blocking positions oriented north toward the city. Company A of the 47th Infantry's 3d Battalion and a battery of artillery from the 3d Battalion, 34th Artillery, were airlifted from Cai Lay to secure the Vinh Long airstrip. The 3d Battalion, 47th Infantry, moved to the east of the 3d Battalion, 60th Infantry, thus completing a blockade across the southern section of Vinh Long.

In the relief of Vinh Long, the 3d Battalion, 60th Infantry, commanded by Lieutenant Colonel Hill, played the major role. The battalion came under small arms fire from a Viet Cong force shortly after landing. Companies A and E of the 3d Battalion, 60th Infantry, called in artillery and moved slowly toward the Viet Cong positions. By late afternoon, Company E had killed seven Viet Cong and captured five weapons. At 2030, however, the unit got into an all-night fight with a heavily armed Viet Cong company southeast of the city. Riverboats of the Mobile Riverine Force patrolled the waterways in the area to contain the enemy.

At dawn both battalions began search operations. The 3d Battalion, 60th Infantry, located thirty-seven dead Viet Cong. Sweep operations continued throughout the day with limited enemy contact. About 1745 hours the battalions boarded the armored troop carriers and moved by river into the Mekong Delta area and on to the afloat base. The tired soldiers and sailors had had eight days and nights of continuous movement and combat.

After a well-deserved night's rest, the riverine force resumed its pursuit of the elusive Viet Cong. Intelligence sources indicated that the Viet Cong were now moving south and west to the Cai Cam River. The 2d Brigade decided to deploy an "eagle float" down the river. This force was an infantry company with supporting fire mounted in armored troop carriers. In conjunction with aircraft overhead, the unit conducted a reconnaissance in force along the Cai Cam, searching for signs of the enemy. When the enemy was sighted, the eagle float moved ashore to search out the Viet Cong. After the operation, the troops quickly loaded back on the boats and got under way again. Shortly before noon the lead minesweepers of the small riverine element received automatic weapon, recoilless rifle, and rocket fire from both banks of the Cai Cam. Company B, 3d Battalion, 60th Infantry, beached immediately on the west side of the river and swept to the south. Finding no enemy troops, the company returned to the river. At midafternoon, both Companies B and E put ashore to search again for the Viet Cong. They came under enemy fire from rockets, rifle grenades, and 60-mm. mortars. Company B assaulted the Viet Cong position, killing five of the enemy, while armed helicopters, artillery, and the Navy riverboats provided fire support. As the Viet Cong retreated, Company A joined the action. To assist in trapping the enemy, the battalion commander asked Colonel David to send the 2d Brigade's ready-reaction force into the battle area. Within minutes, the men of Company B, 3d Battalion, 47th Infantry, had boarded boats and were en route to the Cai Cam River. The company arrived about 1900 hours and landed under the control of Colonel Hill. At dusk, night defensive positions were established by all units as the fighting came to a stop. The eagle float, reinforced by the Mobile Riverine Force, had killed sixty-three of the enemy, while losing four U.S. soldiers. Twenty-seven weapons were captured along with medical supplies, ammunition, and documents. On the morning of 7 February Colonel David deployed the remainder of the 3d Battalion, 47th Infantry, into the Cai Cam area. Both battalions searched the previous day's battlefield and moved southward to look for the fleeing enemy. During the day, seventeen retreating Viet Cong were killed and five weapons were captured. Both battalions loaded onto armored troop carriers and returned to the afloat base on the Mekong River.

During the period 29 January to 7 February, the Mobile Riverine Force had made three major relocations. The 2d Brigade was sent from western Dinh Tuong Province to relieve My Tho, to the north to secure Cai Lay, and finally to the southwest to protect the city of Vinh Long. After moving by boat and helicopter the soldiers of the 2d

EAGLE FLOAT OF MOBILE RIVERINE FORCE *beaches to search for Viet Cong.*

Brigade fought through city streets and through the muck and mire of the swamps to meet the enemy. The quick response of the riverine force and the well-co-ordinated fire from Navy rivercraft, barge-mounted artillery, tactical aircraft, and helicopter gunships turned the Viet Cong offensive into a disastrous defeat. The Mobile Riverine Force was again aboard the ships of their afloat base, awaiting orders for deployment in the Mekong Delta.

The 9th Infantry Division was highly successful in adapting unit organizations, equipment, and tactics to meet the challenge of the delta's terrain and of the Viet Cong's ability to blend in with the people of the villages. "Jitterbug and seal" operations were examples of the tactical innovations aimed at reconnaissance and encirclement of elusive enemy elements. Planning for these special maneuvers started at division headquarters approximately one week before an operation. A series of targets was selected and intelligence efforts were focused on these areas. Commanders at all levels immersed themselves in the details of the intelligence process to insure a thorough understanding of enemy movements and patterns in their areas of operation. The day before a jitterbug and seal operation, the battalion to perform the mission was briefed on the probable targets and assigned air cavalry and airmobile support. The brigade commander would not select the specific targets until the evening before the operation so that the latest intelligence could be used. He would then choose five to seven targets for the jitterbug and seal operation. Tactical air strikes were planned in advance, and artillery was moved to cover the new targets. Orders were issued to the mission battalion, which in turn prepared two companies for the assault.

The next morning final co-ordination was completed and the mission was under way. At the first target, a helicopter with an airborne personnel detector aboard swept the area at tree-top level. Cobra gunships orbited at 500 to 700 feet, looking for fleeing Viet Cong. Scout helicopters hovered above the area and searched for bunkers, trails, or signs of movement. If the enemy's presence was suspected, riot control agents were placed on the targets, and scout helicopter pilots, wearing protective masks, hovered their aircraft near the ground, using the prop wash to spread the agent. If enemy bunkers were seen, the Cobras made firing passes to make the Viet Cong expose themselves.

Meanwhile, the first lift of a rifle company was in the air ready for action. If enemy contact was made, the battalion commander evaluated the target information and determined what size force to send into the objective area. When light enemy resistance was indicated, only five troop helicopters would land. If a large enemy force was met, the entire jitterbug force would assault the target. As the jitterbug force attacked, successive helicopter lifts encircled, or sealed, the target. All available firepower was brought to bear. As soon as the battalion's contact began to show promise, the brigade commander assumed control and alerted one of his battalions to begin sealing in the Viet Cong. The encircled enemy force was then pounded by artillery and air strikes. Canals and rivers were sealed off with concertina wire stretched from one bank to the other. Hand grenades were thrown into streams every five or ten minutes to discourage escape.

BARGE-MOUNTED 105-MM. HOWITZER

After several hours of bombardment, all fire was halted, and the Viet Cong were asked to surrender. Firing was resumed after the brief pause if the enemy refused.

If the enemy was located, a battalion could conduct as many as five jitterbug and seal operations a day. If no contact with the enemy developed, the battalion could search fifteen to eighteen targets a day. The 9th Infantry Division learned that when brigades performed the jitterbug and seal with skill, the ratio of enemy to friendly losses rose dramatically.

One of the problems encountered in the marshy areas of the Mekong Delta was finding suitable firing positions for artillery pieces. The 9th Infantry Division solved the problem by mounting 105-mm. howitzers on landing craft and barges that could accompany the infantry. Both direct and indirect fire could be delivered from these floating platforms. For indirect fire support, the landing craft, mechanized, was run up on a sloping bank and tied to stumps and trees. The barges mounted with artillery were secured against a steep bank in deeper water. In both cases, procedures governing the accuracy and direction of fire were the same as on land. Direct fire was particularly valuable in providing security for riverine troop movement. It was also often used to prepare intended landing sites for the floating infantry. These variations provided the artillery with a significant extension of its capability in the delta.

Division commanders in Vietnam found the helicopter to be an effective instrument for deceiving the enemy. In an airmobile operation the commander was able to concentrate or disperse his forces quickly for tactical advantage. The same speed and flexibility was often applied in a feint to distract the enemy from the real airmobile objective or to lead him into a position favorable to the airmobile force. An enemy observer was deceived when artillery preparations and air strikes were directed on possible landing zones, followed by the false landing of a flight of helicopters, which then quickly turned and flew to the actual objective. Sometimes the aircraft would touch down in a landing zone with the soldier-passengers clearly visible. As the helicopter lifted out of the landing zone, the soldiers would lie on the floor of the helicopter giving the impression that the ground forces had unloaded.

The 9th Infantry Division used the helicopter to deceive the Viet Cong in many instances. When a jitterbug and seal operation was completed, helicopters would pick up the airmobile forces to either return them to base or move them to a new target. During several operations a false pickup was staged, leaving a portion of the force in the area to conduct ambushes or patrols. The division also used false helicopter landings to fix a Viet Cong force. To hold the Viet Cong in place, false landings were made along probable withdrawal routes to make the enemy feel that he was surrounded.

At about 0800 hours one morning, a 9th Infantry Division battalion had been conducting a reconnaissance in force when suddenly the men heard the unmistakable sound of rifle fire. Instinctively the point man hit the ground and rolled for cover, but there was only silence. Just one shot had been fired. Somewhere out there was a Viet Cong sniper. The point man surveyed the area; the only possible location for a sniper was in a wood line about 700 meters in front of him. He summoned the radio operator and reported the sniper fire to his platoon leader. A short time later the report reached the battalion commander, who immediately deployed his own sniper team to the point man's location. With its optical equipment the sniper team began a search of the tree line. Finally, the Viet Cong sniper was discovered in a tree 720 meters away. While one team member judged the wind using the M49 spotting scope, the other man fired one shot, killing the Viet Cong sniper.

The use of the sniper was not new in Vietnam, but the systematic training and employment of an aggressive, offensive sniper team—a carefully designed "weapon system"—was. A sniper was no longer just the man in the rifle squad who carried the sniper rifle; he was the product of an established school. According to Major General Donn R. Pepke, Commanding General, 4th Infantry Division: ". . . a two week course was designed to train marksmen from each maneuver unit. Each student was armed with an accurized M14 rifle with a sniper scope mounted. This weapon was retained by the individual when he completed the course and returned to his unit." The original sniper school in Vietnam was established at the 9th Infantry Division in June 1968. The cadre consisted of one major and eight noncommissioned officers from the Army marksmanship training unit at Fort Benning, Georgia. They had extensive experience in competitive shooting, and one was a practiced gunsmith familiar with the techniques for tuning the accuracy of the M14. A training facility was constructed to accommodate thirty students. This facility included a rifle range on which targets were located up to 900 yards away.

Students for the sniper program were selected from volunteers who had qualified as expert riflemen. They were well-motivated soldiers and, in some cases, had competitive marksmanship experience. The training was so rigorous that only 50 percent of the students successfully completed the course.

The initial equipment consisted of National Match Grade M14 rifles. These rifles were glass bedded into impregnated stocks that were impervious to water. The rifles were carefully tuned to achieve a high degree of accuracy. Finally, the sniper used 7.62-mm. National Match Grade ammunition to further insure accurate firing. The selection of the M14 as the sniper rifle to be used in Vietnam was not hastily made. In early 1967 an evaluation was conducted by the U.S. Army Concept Team in Vietnam (ACTIV) to "determine the organizational, doctrinal, and materiel requirements for sniper operations." This evaluation determined that the "accurized M14 was a suitable sniper rifle for Vietnam." Several telescope sights were also tested with various degrees of success. The best sight was an adjustable power telescope that incorporated a range-finding feature. The magnification ranged from three to nine power as desired by the man firing the gun.

The most successful use of the sniper was with ambush patrols. Snipers would either accompany a platoon on an ambush or, when provided with a security element of five to eight men, establish their own ambush-sniper position. They were situated in many cases near known or suspected rice caches or tunnel entrances. Using such tactics, the sniper picked the time and place to engage the enemy, thereby maintaining the initiative. In addition, sniper teams were sometimes left behind to engage Viet Cong who were following a moving unit. The team established positions that would allow long-range observation over the route that the unit had traveled. This technique was effective because the sniper could engage targets as far away as

900 meters and because the Viet Cong tended to be lax about their cover at extreme ranges. Thus, the Viet Cong presented excellent targets. Snipers could also operate at night with the help of "pink light," an infrared searchlight that illuminated an area for a person looking through a starlight scope. This method allowed the sniper to operate anytime of the day or night.

Sniper teams were used against Viet Cong tax collectors, who came from Cambodia to collect taxes from farmers. The stay-behind sniper teams, consisting of two snipers, a radio operator, and three Popular Force soldiers, were dropped off during mechanized infantry operations near the border. The teams remained in position until dusk. According to the villagers in the area, the amount of enemy taxation was greatly reduced. Snipers were also used to prevent the enemy from re-entering areas that he commonly mined or roadblocked.

The effectiveness of the first graduates of the 9th Division's sniper school was immediately apparent. They were assigned to maneuver battalions on 7 November 1968 and made their first enemy kill on 10 November. Through 10 March 1969 the 54 snipers of the 9th Infantry Division made 135 contacts with the enemy, which resulted in 211 confirmed enemy kills. Lieutenant General Julian J. Ewell, the division commander, commented, "The most effective single program we had was the sniper program."

In 1968 the 9th Infantry Division tested the first Army vehicle specifically designed to meet the combat needs of military units operating in the delta: the air cushion vehicle (ACV). The limited road nets, extensive waterway systems, and seasonal flooding of land areas of the delta made an amphibious craft very desirable.

The air cushion vehicle is a modified Bell Aerosystem commercial craft. It is thirty-nine feet long and sixteen feet high. The vehicle is supported by a cushion of high-volume, low-pressure compressed air generated by a centrifugal lift fan. As the fan builds up air pressure in the cushion, the vehicle is lifted. It is almost frictionless when on the air cushion, allowing easy propulsion up to a speed of seventy-five knots. The same engine that powers the lift fan also drives a nine-foot, three-blade propeller that makes the craft speed over the delta terrain. To maintain enough air under the ACV for it to clear obstacles, flexible rubber canvas skirts are hung from the edge of the vehicle to within a fraction of an inch off the ground. The vehicle can clear solid obstacles up to 3½ feet high and rice paddy dikes, with sloping sides, up to 6 feet high. The air cushion vehicle can force its way through grasses and small trees and navigate ditches and canals.

The 9th Infantry Division tested the air cushion vehicle in combat operations against the Viet Cong in the same delta region that was the scene for CORONADO X. In twenty offensive operations, the vehicle traveled over land, swamps, rivers, and the South China Sea at speeds up to seventy knots. The craft mounted machine guns and a high-velocity grenade launcher and carried ten to twelve soldiers. During the test, 43 Viet Cong were killed and 100 detained. Casualties of the ACV units were two soldiers wounded. The craft also performed successfully in security missions and in transport of troops and cargo. The 9th Infantry Division concluded that the air cushion vehicle was suitable for combat operations in the delta and recommended that more vehicles be deployed to Vietnam.

By the end of CORONADO X, the Mobile Riverine Force had again proved its value by moving rapidly and efficiently through difficult terrain to relieve the cities of My Tho and Vinh Long and to pursue the enemy forces. This operation demonstrated many tactical and materiel innovations that were the result of the resourcefulness and originality of the 9th Infantry Division and supporting Navy elements. Mounting the riverine artillery on barges and platforms substantially increased the effectiveness of the force. Such fire support coupled with the mobility provided by the riverine craft, air cushion vehicles, and helicopters made the eagle float and the jitterbug and seal tactics possible. In addition, the mobility, firepower, and imaginative tactical concepts of the riverine forces seized the initiative from the enemy and vastly improved the security of the waterways for South Vietnamese citizens.

CHAPTER VII

Dak To (November-December 1967)

The overwhelming success of U.S. arms at Dak To may be attributed in part to a number of innovations that had been developed by the forces supporting the infantry. Foremost among these were the new and vastly improved communication systems available at division level and below. Commanders were able to achieve greater control and provide better and more responsive support for maneuver units. Also the servicing of helicopters in forward areas contributed greatly to the effectiveness of airmobile operations. Engineer efforts to clear routes of communications and to deny the enemy cover and concealment were supplemented by the use of herbicides and a new "people sniffer."

The battle for Dak To during November and December 1967 was a disaster for the 1st North Vietnamese Army Division. Although the enemy had expected to gain an important psychological victory by swiftly striking western Kontum Province from border sanctuaries, his four fresh regiments were decisively defeated in what a ranking Communist officer termed a "useless and bloody battle." In a classic example of allied superiority in firepower and maneuver, fifteen U.S. and Vietnamese battalions beat the enemy to the punch and sent the survivors limping back to their sanctuaries.

The command and control and communications effort at Dak To was enormous. The 4th Infantry Division headquarters controlled its 1st and 2d Brigades, division artillery, division troops, division support command, the 173d Airborne Brigade, the 1st Brigade of the 1st Cavalry Division (Airmobile), and a myriad of attached and supporting units. The statistics in the three-week battle were impressive: Army aviation flew more than 13,000 hours; eighteen U.S. and Vietnamese artillery batteries fired more than 170,000 rounds; and the Air Force executed 2,100 tactical air and 300 B-52 sorties. Four enemy regiments lost 1,644 known dead.

The battle can be described best in the words of Major General William R. Peers, who was the Commanding General, 4th Infantry Division, during the operation:

The 'battle for DAK TO' was not a designated operation in itself, but occurred within the boundaries of the 4th Infantry Division's Operation MACARTHUR. . . . Nevertheless, the size of the two opposing forces, the length and violence of the engagement and the overall significance of the battle have made the events that occurred in the vicinity of DAK TO from 2 October to 1 December the most important that have occurred in the Central Highlands since the 1954 Geneva Convention. . . .

By late October intelligence sources began detecting unusual and large movements in the tri-border area—the junction of LAOTIAN-CAMBODIAN-SOUTH VIETNAMESE borders—west of the DAK TO Special Forces Camp in KONTUM Province. As the area was watched by the various means of aerial and ground intelligence gathering agencies it became apparent that the NVA was moving large forces into southwest KONTUM Province. . . .

The 1st Brigade, which had been surveilling the border area in western PLEIKU Province, began deploying to new [*sic*] DAK TO airfield on 28 October. On 2 November an NVA reconnaissance sergeant became a CHIEU HOI and divulged what later proved to be the accurate positions and battle plans of the four NVA infantry regiments and one artillery regiment that were preparing to launch the largest enemy attack to date in the Central Highlands against the DAK TO-TAN CANH area. The NVA sergeant revealed that the enemy plan was to launch the primary attack with two regiments from the south and southwest of DAK TO supported by mortar and rocket fire. A second attack into the area, also supported by rockets and mortars, was to be launched from the northeast by one regiment. The fourth regiment was to be held in reserve. This information proved to be correct and was valuable in the initial deployment of our forces. The 1st Brigade sent one battalion on to the ridgeline that runs east to west south of DAK TO and an OPCON battalion from the 173d Airborne Brigade moved west and established a fire support base for medium artillery at BEN HET.

The initial contacts were made on the ridgeline south of DAK TO by the 3d Battalion, 12th Infantry; followed in succession by very heavy contacts to the southwest by the 3d Battalion, 8th Infantry, and by the 4th Battalion, 503d Airborne Infantry moving south from BEN HET. This initial phase took place from 1-6 November and can be viewed as the brigade's forces attacking into the face of enemy units as they were moving toward preselected and in some areas previously prepared positions. After these initial contacts the 173d Airborne Brigade with two battalions arrived at DAK TO and moved west to BEN HET. During this phase from 7 to 12 November, contact was continuous as battalions were combat assaulted behind the lead elements and into the base areas of the 32d and 66th NVA Regiments.

Meanwhile, the ARVN Forces placed their units in vicinity of TAN CAHN to the east of DAK TO. A battalion of the 42d ARVN Regiment, later joined by the 2d and 3d ARVN Airborne Battalions, oriented to the north and northeast to initially block and then attack the 24th NVA Regiment moving on to the DAK TO-TAN CANH area from the northeast down the TUMERONG Valley. The 2d Battalion, 8th Cavalry, moved into an AO southeast of TAN CANH to react against a possible attack from the southeast against the now large base complex along Route 512 from TAN CANH to DAK TO. The 1st Brigade, 1st Air Cavalry Division with the 1st Battalion, 12th Cavalry, arrived at KONTUM from the coast and was immediately deployed into the DAK HODRAI Valley south of the main battle area to intercept the withdrawing NVA.

The NVA forces were stopped and forced to withdraw. To the west of the BEN HET the NVA committed their reserves, the 174th NVA Regiment, to cover the withdrawal to the southwest of their two hard hit regiments. This resulted in the violent, four day struggle for Hill 875 which ultimately involved two battalions of the 173d Airborne Brigade and the 1st Battalion, 12th Infantry, which was airlifted into the battle area from DARLAC Province. The hill was taken after receiving . . . TAC air and . . . artillery bombardment. . . . Meanwhile, northeast of TAN CANH an ARVN infantry battalion fixed a large NVA force on a hill mass while two ARVN airborne battalions swept up the flanks in a fierce two day battle, which inflicted heavy NVA casualties. Later, the same 2d and 3d ARVN Airborne Battalions sprang an attempted enemy ambush with one battalion while getting behind the positioned NVA forces with the other battalion and hitting the headquarters group, completely routing the battalion-size force.

One of the means by which the division located and kept track of the enemy was the airborne personnel detector, commonly referred to as the "people sniffer." This air-transportable electrochemical instrument sensed microscopic particles suspended in the air. Mounted in the utility or light observation helicopters, the detector continuously sampled the atmosphere at the flight altitude of the aircraft for evidence of the enemy. It could also detect the ammonia excretions of men.

The improvement in communications available to the field commander in Vietnam stands as a hallmark of accomplishment of Army communications personnel at all levels. Insight into the communications situation is given by Brigadier General William M. Van Harlingen, Jr., in his debriefing report after eighteen months as commanding general of the 1st Signal Brigade:

> Communications has been a significant factor in the conflict in Vietnam. The enemy's limited tactical communications capability has forced him to adhere to preplanned offensive operations and denied to him the flexibility needed to react to the changing circumstances of battle. On the other hand our wealth of tactical communications has given us great flexibility and permitted us to use our tactical mobility to the fullest advantage. Communications organic to our divisions and field forces, along with substantial support by combat area signal units, have given U.S. field commanders a command and control capability which, along with their overwhelming firepower and tactical mobility has permitted them a freedom of action which they have exploited to the fullest in the conduct of operations.

The advances in communications since the Korean War have contributed immeasurably to the over-all effectiveness of the U.S. Army in combat. Through the extensive communication systems at each level, commanders were better able to control the personnel and weapons under their command. The communication improvement resulted from a number of factors, including the evolution in electronics technology that caused the vacuum tube to give way to transistor–solid state circuitry.

Because wire and cable were obviously not suitable for interconnecting widely separated units across unsecured areas, VHF radio relay became the backbone of division communications. Responsive

MOCK-UP OF XM-2 (MODIFIED E63) AIRBORNE PERSONNEL DETECTOR *mounted on UH-1 aircraft.*

telephone service was provided to all parties who genuinely needed it. Multichannel VHF connections extended from brigade to battalion level, using division resources. Howitzer batteries supporting infantry battalions were allocated patch-through circuits from these radio relays, and alternate routes and backup systems were used extensively during tactical operations.

Typically, the organic division's communications were augmented by the Field Force Signal Battalion and by the area system provided by the 1st Signal Brigade for use by all friendly forces. These supplements were required by the great size of the division's usual area of operations and by the terrain that posed many challenges to the communicator. The significant innovation in the area system was the provision of multichannel VHF radio relay to small units. According to published doctrine, corps (field forces) systems terminated at artillery group level, but in Vietnam, field forces sometimes provided multichannel service as far down as the artillery battery. This extension not only improved communications but also supported sole-user telephone service (hot lines) anywhere the commander desired. The actual use of the system varied greatly from division to division. The tactical operations center of the 1st Infantry Division was typical. It had thirty-five sole-user circuits that terminated in the operations center. In World War II four channels of communication ran from a corps to a division, while in the Korean War the use of eight channels from a corps to a division was standard practice. In Vietnam, however, thirty-two channels to a single combat brigade were common. This tremendous improvement in battlefield communications had a proportionate effect on the commander's ability to influence the battle.

Large-scale airmobile operations in Vietnam allowed, and virtually required, the commander to move his command post from the ground to the air. Effective command and control of widespread units in the jungle was not possible from the traditional command post of previous wars. An airborne command post was the solution. A critical component of this new command post was the communications equipment available to the commander and his staff. Several early configurations had been tried; in 1965 a basic console was approved that included two FM radios, one VHF radio, one UHF radio, and one high-frequency, single side band radio. Designated the AN/ASC-6, this console was designed for quick installation and removal. In 1968 the AN/ASC-10 console was developed. This item was smaller and easier to install and provided an intercom system for the command group on board the aircraft. Another new console, the AN/ASC-11, consisted of two vehicular FM radios plus the organic, high-frequency, single side band in the aircraft. Two AN/ASC-11's could be installed in one aircraft. An alternative to the AN/ASC-10 was the AN/ASC-15. It had three UHF-FM radios with a secure voice device.

These radios allowed the commander and his staff to control combat operations. The command group could use several radio nets simultaneously. For example, a Vietnamese commander could use one FM net to control his ground units; the senior U.S. adviser could

AN/ASC-15 COMMUNICATION CENTRAL

communicate with the American advisers on the other FM set; the air liaison officer could maintain UHF contact with the forward air controllers directing the air strikes; and the high-frequency, single side band would be available, if needed, to enter the corps' air support operations net. The commander of the aviation unit could use the helicopter radios to control his aircraft.

The composition of the command group varied depending on the desire of the commander and the nature of the mission. For Vietnamese units, the group often consisted of the Vietnamese commander, his senior U.S. adviser, an air liaison officer, and an artillery adviser. For U.S. units, the command group was made up of the airmobile force commander and his operations officer, air and artillery liaison officers, and sometimes the higher unit commander or a member of his staff. The commander of the U.S. Army aviation unit or his operations officer was normally the pilot or copilot of the helicopter command post.

The flexibility of the helicopter command post enabled the commander to control ground units, to co-ordinate the helicopter force with prestrike forces, to co-ordinate all fire support (attack helicopters, ground support fire, and tactical air), and to perform special missions. In spite of these and other advantages, there were some limitations for the airborne commander. Bad weather caused the helicopter to fly at lower altitudes, thereby increasing its vulnerability to ground fire and causing congestion over the landing zone. The weight of the radio equipment limited the amount of fuel that could be carried. Furthermore, the commander had to decide between carrying more troops and less fuel, which decreased the flying time, and more fuel and fewer troops, which added to the flying time. The size of the helicopter also limited space and facilities. Especially important was the disadvantage of having all key personnel on one helicopter. While these limitations presented problems, the helicopter command post was still an effective command and control vehicle for the type of warfare and terrain found in Vietnam.

The airborne radio relay was an innovation conceived to provide communication links between separated elements beyond the range of normal communication equipment or deployed in terrain that lacked adequate sites for ground relay operations. Some of the configurations used were U1-A and CV-2 aircraft with four channels of communication, using FM radios and ARC-121 consoles; U-21 aircraft with six secure channels of FM communication, using an ARC-149 console; O-1 aircraft with a ground or aircraft FM radio; OH-13 aircraft with aircraft FM radios; and UH-1D aircraft with a ground FM radio. During the first three months of 1966 an airmobile radio relay was used in eighteen of forty-two operations reported by brigades of the 1st Cavalry Division and 1st Infantry Division, by the 173d Airborne Brigade, and by the 1st Brigade, 101st Airborne Division. Specific note of this technique was made by Lieutenant Colonel Tom M. Nicholson, former commanding officer of the 13th Signal Battalion. Colonel Nicholson wrote:

> On many occasions, airborne relay was provided by CV-2 aircraft, which had a capability of 6 relays at once. This multiple relay was used for simultaneous support of the battalion command, the brigade command, the artillery fire, the forward air control, and medical evacuation net, during many operations. The outstanding logistical support and medical evacuation, experienced by the battalions of the 1st Air Cav Division, would have been severely restricted without the airborne relay.

In some situations the bulk and weight of standard equipment configurations proved unsatisfactory, resulting in serious problems in mobility and flexibility. An example of such a situation is the AN/MRC-69 VHF radio relay terminal that provided connection with division telephone and teletype networks. A minimum of two CH-47 helicopter sorties was needed to lift the AN/MRC-69 with its component generator set. After being landed in heavy jungle, the shelter was not mobile and in many cases was operating extremely close to the landing zone. To solve these problems, some units built special re configurations, commonly called MRC-34½ (half of 69). Typically, they consisted of a ¾-ton trailer with enough equipment from the AN/MRC-69 to terminate twelve channels of voice communication links (half of the AN/MRC-69 capacity). As one report on command communications states:

The trailer configuration was chosen because of its several advantages. Though a vehicular mounted set was self transporting, it was deemed too heavy for the intended purpose. Also, the rig could not be employed if the vehicle was deadlined. Finally, a trailer mounted radio terminal was lighter and easier to handle. It could be backed into a Chinook and followed by the skid mounted 3kw generator with little or no trouble.

Before the battle of Dak To, the 4th Infantry Division's communication unit, the 124th Signal Battalion, had had some experience with the MRC-34½. The first MRC-34½ constructed by the 124th Signal Battalion was based on pictures of radio relay units built by another division. Numerous improvements were made on the final version. What resulted was an exceptional, air-transportable communications system, which proved itself in the Dak To operation, according to the after action report of the battle.

Due to inaccessibility of some areas by road movement and also the requirement for immediate communications it was necessary to airlift the AN/MRC-34½ on four different occasions. The first was when the 1st Brigade, 1st Air Cav located a TAC CP at Polei Kleng. From there it was airlifted to the 1st Brigade, 1st Air Cav Div, CP when they displaced to the Dak To area. When they were released from Div OPCON and the 1/12th Air Cav Squadron relocated in the vicinity of Plei Mrong it was again airlifted by chopper and the last time was back to Dak To Airfield when the 173d Abn Brigade assumed OPCON of the 1/12th Cav. This extreme flexibility of movement for 12 channel VHF communications equipment proved once again to be an invaluable assist to this Division.

In 1968 the Nestor program, which included a group of speech security apparatus—KY-8 and KY-38 ground equipment and KY-28 airborne equipment—for FM radios, was introduced. The use of this new equipment was limited at first; however, more command emphasis coupled with attempts to procure missing and desired items increased its use to approximately 85 percent as of June 1970. The HYL-3 Regenerative Repeater was introduced to meet the need for secure retransmission. Over-all, secure voice equipment was an innovation of major importance.

In 1969 a durable, easy-to-use, low-level, numeral, authentication code, the Circe wheel code, patterned after an Air Force wheel code, was designed to replace the existing low-level codes (KAC-Q). The KAC-Q codes had been bulky, easily torn, and time-consuming and, consequently, had promoted the use of unauthorized codes. Field tests of the Circe wheel code by the 23d Infantry Division (Americal) and 1st Brigade, 5th Infantry Division, revealed that the new code was easier to operate and more durable and that it discouraged the use of unauthorized codes.

The battle for Dak To was a logistician's nightmare. The helicopters supporting the operation consumed 863,190 gallons of JP4 fuel and 32,550 gallons of aviation gasoline and used an enormous quantity of ammunition. To sustain this effort, rearm and refuel points were established at Dak To, Kontum, Camp Enari, and Camp Holloway. In the early days of the war, civilian trucks traveled through enemy territory to the forward area of operations where the helicopters were refueled. As the war intensified, this method proved unreliable and inadequate. Experience indicated the need for forward support bases for the rearming and refueling of helicopters. Operations in areas remote from the base camp stood a much better chance of success if the round-trip time of the helicopters could be reduced.

Beginning in January 1966, aviation battalions made good use of Vietnam airfields as logistic bases of operations. This practice placed almost any area of operations within a 25- to 30-nautical-mile radius of an airfield. Each refuel and rearm station was already stocked with the proper munitions, petroleum products, and equipment. Using these stockpiles, the units were able to respond quickly to previously planned and quick-reaction-type operations.

Refueling was accomplished using either 500-gallon bladders or 55-gallon drums and portable pumping equipment. By placing the 500-gallon bladders in line, an entire flight element could refuel in minutes without shutting down. From 1966 through 1968 several equipment changes were prompted by the need to increase the ability of aviation units supporting tactical operations to refuel rapidly. By spring of 1967, aviation units could refuel at a rate of 350 gallons per minute. This system simultaneously refueled twelve UH-1 aircraft within four to six minutes and reduced the average refueling time for the CH-47 by at least ten minutes. One aviation unit reported success with this system using two 10,000-gallon bladders, one 350-gallons-per-minute pump, and a 4-inch manifold with twelve UH-1 and four CH-47 refueling points.

At Dak To there were six 10,000-gallon bladders (two for the CH-47 and four for the UH-1) set up in two JP4 refueling areas. All aviation gas was dispensed from 5,000-gallon trailers. The neoprene bladders with 350-gallons-per-minute pumps and filter-separators were vital elements in the support of combat aircraft.

The refueling and rearming time for gunships could be considerably reduced by keeping small quantities of ammunition at refueling points. Therefore, ammunition was assembled and prepared at one location and transported to the rearming area by ¾-ton trucks. Waste and packing materials were not brought near the aircraft because of the danger to rotor blades. The size of the ¾-ton truck allowed it to move close enough so that the ammunition could be loaded directly onto the helicopter, thus eliminating one handling step. When properly loaded, a ¾-ton truck could carry enough ammunition to rearm several helicopters.

Route 14, the main ground supply route that ran from Pleiku through Kontum to Dak To, passed through many miles of dense growth that grew to within ten feet of the road. This growth provided cover and concealment from which the enemy could ambush a supply column. Early in Operation MACARTHUR the engineers were called on to clear the area on either side of the road. A unique aspect of land clearing in support of tactical operations lay in the amount—in some cases, thousands of acres. The problem was to find equipment that would be both speedy and efficient.

During 1966 and 1967 several methods of land clearing were used. The King Ranch concept—developed on King Ranch property in Australia—consisted of dragging a heavy length of chain (at least fifty pounds per foot) strung between two tractors. For large trees or rocky soil, a steel ball fourteen feet in diameter was placed at the middle of the chain. The technique was found to be especially effective over nonrocky terrain with small-to-medium-diameter trees having shallow roots, but not over land with grasses and light shrubs. The 1st Infantry Division used the King Ranch concept to clear 1,500 trees in four hours. Tests eventually revealed, however, that the division's D7 tractors were too small to pull the anchor chain efficiently. Since very few larger tractors were used in Vietnam, the technique had only limited use.

Another land clearing device, the transphibian tactical crusher, was tested during mid-1967. This massive 97-ton machine used a pusher bar against large trees and cleated drums to chop up felled trees and small vegetation. During testing, trees forty to forty-eight inches in diameter proved to be no obstacle to the crusher. Two crushers were initially used to clear 2,083 acres in the vicinity of Long Binh and then assigned to the 93d Engineer Battalion (Construction) for use in a tactical environment near the Binh Son Rubber Plantation, thirty-five miles southeast of Saigon. Approximately 1,300 acres were cleared in support of the 9th Infantry Division, but the crushers suffered an inordinate amount of time under repair. Therefore, after the testing was completed, no additional crushers were procured.

The equipment that finally filled the need for a rapid, efficient land clearing device was the Rome K/G Clearing Blade—better known as the Rome plow. It consisted of a tractor attachment with a blade that "stung" and "sliced" large trees. A sharp projection on the left side of the blade split the trees, while the cutting edge sheared them off at ground level. The attachment came in two sizes: a 4,600-pound blade that fit the Allis Chalmers HD-16M and Caterpillar

BULLDOZERS WITH ROME PLOWS CLEAR JUNGLE GROWTH *while mechanized infantry stands guard.*

D7E, and smaller 4,000-pound blade used on the airmobile D6B tractor. In late 1966 four Rome plow blades were tested in the 20th Engineer Brigade. They efficiently cleared all vegetation where the soil could support the tractor.

Seventy Rome plow blades were procured for combat engineer units. Although the original purpose of the plow was to clear jungle base areas, it was only a short time before many other uses were found. For example, this land clearing equipment provided a quick way to clear fields of fire around base camps and fire support bases and to construct helicopter landing zones and night defensive positions. The clearing of all vegetation from within 100 to 200 meters of roads significantly reduced the very serious problem of enemy ambush.

Before August 1967, Route 13 north of Lai Khe was completely controlled by the Viet Cong. Field positions and outposts in the northern section of the area depended on aerial resupply, and only rarely did a convoy chance running the road. Occasionally, when this section of Route 13 was opened to support an operation or to resupply Quan Loi or Loc Ninh, extensive engineer efforts and large security forces were required. Radio Hanoi boasted that this road would never again be used for South Vietnamese and American traffic. To meet this challenge and to deny cover and concealment to the enemy, a combat engineer battalion used six bulldozers equipped with land clearing blades and heavy steel cabs for the operators' protection. Working with armored security forces, the bulldozers peeled back the jungle 200 meters on both sides of Route 13. Concurrently engineer work parties repaired culverts, craters, and bridges in an extensive effort to improve this route for division traffic. On 1 November 1967, during Operation SHENANDOAH II, Route QL 13 was opened for resupply convoys.

Initially, an enormous amount of manpower was required to secure the road. This need tied down many units of an infantry division and limited the number of battalions available for conducting other offensive operations. Again the bulldozers with land clearing blades solved the problem by cutting night defensive positions having wide fields of fire at 4- to 5-kilometer intervals along the road. These positions were then fortified with enough troops and equipment to sweep and secure the road each day. Early in 1968 the bulldozers pushed back the jungle an additional 200 meters on each side of Route QL 13, thus reducing night defensive positions by 50 percent.

The first major combat support clearing operation was conducted in the Iron Triangle area during Operations NIAGARA FALLS and CEDAR FALLS, when 3,000 acres were cleared. During Operation PAUL BUNYAN, the 168th Engineer Battalion cleared over 14,000 acres in support of the 1st Infantry Division.

The land clearing organization grew from a few isolated tractors to a battalion-size operation. In mid-1967 three land clearing teams, composed of thirty Rome plow blades, mounted on D7E tractors, and sixty-four men, were activated and attached to the 27th, 86th, and 35th Engineer Battalions. Their success led to the formation of six land clearing companies. Finally, the 62d Engineer Battalion (Construction) was reorganized and equipped as a land clearing battalion. By October 1969 the engineers had cleared 388,852 acres.

Since the beginning of land clearing operations, enemy sanctuaries, base camps, and infiltration routes have been exposed, and the enemy has been separated from local supply sources and tax-collection points. Land cleared by Rome plows has been immediately available for farming and resettling, particularly along the major lines of communication. Wood for cooking and heating has been easily obtainable, and a potential exists for the development of lumber production.

Defoliation operations also deprived the enemy of his hiding places. Although they later became the center of much controversy, herbicides were important tactical weapons. Defoliation and crop destruction were first tested as counterinsurgency measures in 1961 as a part of Project AGILE, a joint U.S.-South Vietnamese development program. Chemical spray tests were made by the Vietnamese Air Force with experimental dissemination devices and off-the-shelf commercial herbicides. Despite the serious limitations of the components, the results demonstrated clearly that available growth-regulator and desiccant chemicals were capable of defoliating tropical forests and destroying enemy food crops. The first U.S. Air Force C-123/MC-1 (Hourglass) spray system, along with herbicide agents Purple and Blue, reached Vietnam in 1962, and Operation RANCH HAND was initiated to conduct defoliation and anticrop operations.

By the time of the U.S. buildup in 1965-1966, the two agents most commonly used in RANCH HAND were Blue and Orange, so named for the color markings on the containers in which the herbicides were shipped. Orange is a mixture of two relatively common herbicides (2, 4-D and 2, 4, 5-T) and is classified as a systemic herbicide. As such it is absorbed into the plant from the point of application. Once inside the plant's system, Orange interferes with the growth processes, such as photosynthesis, and eventually kills the plant if the dose is adequate. Blue is a desiccant, contact herbicide that damages plant tissue at the point where it is applied. Desiccants are drying agents that will cause leaves to drop off but will not necessarily kill the plant itself. In Vietnam new foliage may grow back within thirty to ninety days after applying Blue.

The rather complicated procedures and safeguards governing approval for operational use of herbicides in South Vietnam were set forth in MACV Directive 525-1. The use of herbicides for defoliation and crop destruction was primarily an operation of the government of South Vietnam, supported by U.S. assets and expertise. Under policy guidance established by the U.S. Departments of State and Defense, the Commander, U.S. Military Assistance Command, Vietnam, and the U.S. Ambassador were empowered jointly to authorize U.S. support of the South Vietnamese government's requests for herbicide operations. General co-ordination of the program and guidance was the responsibility of the Chemical Operations Division of MACV's J-3 (Operations Directorate).

All requests for fixed-wing aircraft defoliation and for fixed-wing, helicopter, and ground spray crop destruction originated at the district or province level. These requests were processed through ARVN division and corps tactical zones to the Joint General Staff of the Republic of Vietnam armed forces. Simultaneously, U.S. commanders and advisers involved in the project were submitting their views through channels to MACV's J-3. Requests approved by the Vietnamese Joint General Staff in their 203 Committee were then passed to the chemical operation division of MACV's J-3, where the approved project was consolidated with the position of the U.S. commanders and advisers before being submitted to the U.S. 203 Committee. This committee consisted of representatives from MACV's J-3, J-2, and Psychological Operations section and from Operation RANCH HAND, Civil Operations and Revolutionary Development Support (CORDS), U.S. Agency for International Development (USAID), Joint U.S. Public Affairs Office (JUSPAO), and the American Embassy. After reviewing each project, as well as necessary U.S. support, the U.S. 203 Committee forwarded its recommendation to the MACV commander and the U.S. Ambassador for consideration. If they approved the project for support, the Joint General Staff was notified, and a co-ordination meeting was held in the capital of the province concerned. The province chief who sponsored the meeting was joined by the U.S. province and corps advisers, MACV's Chemical Operations Division action officer, Joint General Staff representatives, and RANCH HAND personnel. Final details and changes in previous requests were made, and special conditions required during spray operations were established. The Joint General Staff then published an operation order for the project and established target priorities. They requested that U.S. support be provided on order. Details of the co-ordination of U.S. support were provided by the Chemical Operations Division to the commander of the Seventh Air Force and to the 12th Special Operations Squadron. A final opportunity was given to the province chief to cancel the mission twenty-four to forty-eight hours before the individual mission was executed.

U.S. and Vietnamese corps commanders jointly were authorized to carry out helicopter defoliation operations approved by the province chief and the U.S. senior adviser. These operations were conducted to support local base defense, to maintain Rome-plowed areas, and to clear known ambush sites along lines of communication. Vietnamese corps commanders and their U.S. senior advisers could approve requests for defoliation with ground-based equipment.

During the battle for Dak To, the 2d Battalion, 503d Infantry, of the 173d Airborne Brigade, established a fire support base in an area of dense vegetation. The brigade's chemical section conducted three defoliation missions close to the fire support base in an attempt to deprive the enemy of cover for ground or standoff attacks. The defoliation of allied base perimeters was usually carried out by ground or helicopter spray. The spraying had to be increased during the growing season. Because of the 400-gallon metal tank in the CH-47 and the use of pressurized bottles to refill the tanks in flight, 700 to 800 gallons of defoliant could be delivered in a single sortie.

Defoliation along the lines of communication, with emphasis on ambush sites and tax-collecting points, was quite effective in opening these areas and improving aerial observation. On two occasions defoliation operations reportedly disrupted Viet Cong ambushes by forcing the enemy to move out of the area as soon as it had been sprayed. The defoliation of infiltration routes greatly inhibited the enemy's movement during the daylight hours, because he feared detection from the air. On several occasions defoliation forced unplanned moves because it affected the protective tree foliage within six hours. The spraying of herbicides on enemy base areas kept the Viet Cong and North Vietnamese Army on the move and forced them to avoid defoliated areas for fear of detection.

The destruction of crops intended for the enemy was another significant accomplishment of the herbicide operations. This type of operation had, in some instances, forced the enemy to divert tactical units from combat missions to food procurement tasks. The resulting food shortages among enemy ranks prompted some defections. Defoliation accounted for approximately 90 percent of the herbicide effort in Vietnam. The remaining 10 percent was devoted to crop destruction.

In January 1968, a Herbicide Review Committee was established at the direction of U.S. Ambassador Ellsworth Bunker to conduct a comprehensive review of each aspect of the U.S.-South Vietnamese herbicide program. Subcommittees were organized to study defoliation and crop destruction.

In its findings, the defoliation subcommittee "recognized the military worth of defoliation beyond any doubt." The program was important in denying the enemy cover in heavily forested areas such as War Zones C and D and in Boi Loi Woods. It also increased the security of all allied forces by eliminating foliage around base camps and at likely ambush sites along water and land routes of communication. Captured Viet Cong and *Chieu Hois* who were questioned about the effects of defoliation admitted that their units often avoided crossing defoliated areas and would not camp in them. One soldier indicated that his unit had been prevented from occupying ambush sites along a canal because of defoliation operations.

The subcommittee made note of the economic and psychological costs of the program by calling attention to the possible loss of valuable stands of timber in War Zones C and D which would be unavoidable unless salvage operations were begun within two years. It also expressed concern over the success of the Viet Cong in promoting propaganda about the program which reflected adversely on U.S. motives and actions. The committee called for improved operational and program controls to minimize the effect of herbicide drift on crops near target areas.

The subcommittee on crop destruction found that such operations had been successful in weakening enemy strength and in denying food to the Viet Cong and North Vietnamese Army military units.

RESULT OF DEFOLIATION OPERATIONS *along canal and secondary road.*

In some cases when food crops were destroyed, civilians who were supporting the communists were compelled to seek refuge in areas controlled by the government of South Vietnam, thereby depriving the enemy of labor as well as food. Communist military forces were then compelled to raise their own crops which detracted from their operational mission. Food-growing detachments were forced to work harder, and the results were poor. Frequently, subsistence had to be obtained elsewhere to sustain an additional burden to the already strained communist transportation system.

However, evidence also indicated that since the civilian population in Viet Cong–controlled areas inevitably bore the brunt of crop destruction operations, considerable adverse political and psychological costs were incurred. The subcommittee called attention to the fact that the use of herbicides was only part of the total food denial program. Consequently, if crops were destroyed while other sources of food remained available, then the program was less effective. The committee found that past food control and denial activities had not been sufficiently co-ordinated at mission level and, therefore, had not realized their full potential.

As a result of the committee's findings and conclusions, the defoliation and crop destruction programs were continued, but tighter control measures were imposed.

By the end of 1968, the most intensive defoliation efforts had been made in the infamous Rung Sat Special Zone, which surrounded the shipping channel into Saigon and in War Zones C and D. A survey of these areas was conducted in March and April 1968 by Fred H. Tchirley, an expert in the Agricultural Research Division of the U.S. Department of Agriculture. He concluded at the time that the defoliation program, especially in the areas of intense treatment, had caused ecological changes. He did not feel that such changes were irreversible but, as he said, ". . . recovery may take a long time. . . ." For example, regeneration of the mangrove forests in the Rung Sat was estimated to require about twenty years. Mr. Tchirley made no prediction on the semideciduous forests, such as those found in War Zones C and D. He said:

> A single treatment on semideciduous forest would cause inconsequential change. Repeated treatments will result in invasion of many sites by bamboo. . . . The time scale of regeneration of semideciduous forest is unknown. Available information is so scanty that a prediction would have no validity and certainly no real meaning. Most of the defoliation treatments in semideciduous forests have been made along lines of communication. The ecological effect of defoliation in those areas would not be as severe as in areas where large blocks have been treated.

In April 1970, the Department of Defense ordered a temporary ban on the use of agent Orange. This restriction resulted in a corresponding decrease in the number of defoliation missions flown, and by July 1970 all defoliation missions by fixed-wing aircraft were halted. Crop destruction missions, although never flown in the rice-producing delta, were also severely curtailed and then stopped completely a short time later.

There were a number of articles in scientific magazines in 1969 and 1970 that criticized the U.S. government's herbicide program in Vietnam. The Herbicide Assessment Commission of the American Association for the Advancement of Science (AAAS) made a five-week inspection tour of Vietnam in the summer of 1970. The commission, headed by Harvard biologist Matthew S. Meselson, asserted that the spraying program had caused "extremely serious harm" to the land and to "some of the peoples of the war-torn country." In addition to condemning the destruction of the mangrove and hardwood forests, Meselson's group charged that the crop destruction effort was a failure and that spraying may have been responsible for a high number of stillbirths and birth defects among the Vietnamese in 1967 and 1968. The commission did stress that "neither effect could safely be attributed to the impact of herbicides." It felt that further studies were necessary to determine the cause of medical phenomenon in children born of women who lived in heavily sprayed areas. Meselson indicated that the focus for future action "should be shifted away from assessing harm and toward finding ways to repair the damage done."

A number of other articles had been written which seemed to

imply that Indochina had been totally destroyed by herbicides and that all spraying was done without plan or purpose. The AAAS commission found that there was a "spectrum of opinion" on the military usefulness of the program but did not discuss the improved security for civilians and allied forces along lines of communications after spraying operations.

In October 1970, Congress passed a bill which became Public Law 91-441. One provision of this law directed the Secretary of Defense to ". . . enter into appropriate arrangements with the National Academy of Sciences to conduct a comprehensive study and investigation to determine (a) the ecological and physiological dangers inherent in the use of herbicides, and (b) the ecological and physiological effects of the defoliation program carried out by the Department of Defense in South Vietnam. . . ." The National Academy of Sciences (NAS) report was to be completed by 31 January 1972 and forwarded to the President and the Congress "with such comments and recommendations as . . . appropriate" by 1 March 1972. Until the findings of the academy are made public, and perhaps even afterward, speculation about the detrimental effects of herbicides in Vietnam will probably continue to be debated. Vietnam has certainly not been destroyed, as some critics claim, and many U.S. soldiers are alive today because of the defoliation of ambush sites and the uncovering of enemy base areas.

In addition to taking away the enemy's hiding places, U.S. forces developed methods to conceal their own operations. In early 1966 a method was developed to dispense smoke from a low-flying helicopter so that all or part of a landing zone could be obscured from the enemy's view to protect landing helicopters. The first system used a UH-1C "Hog" gunship with its M3 rocket system mounted backwards. Smoke grenade canisters were inserted into the rocket launcher tubes and ejected to the rear as the aircraft flew at a slow speed and close to the ground. This method proved to be satisfactory if the landing zone was not inundated.

The integral smoke generator, XM-52, was designed to produce a dense cloud of smoke by injecting atomized fog oil into the hot exhaust gases of the turbine engine of the UH-1. The oil was immediately vaporized, and smoke billowed to the rear. One 60-gallon tank or two 55-gallon bladders were used; the bladders provided eight minutes of smoke. The smoke generator proved to be so successful that a contract was awarded for the manufacture of 121 systems. In addition to its use in landing zones during combat assaults, smoke could be dispensed along a flight route to screen helicopter movement, in landing zones during medical evacuations, and in unused landing zones as a diversionary tactic.

The battle for Dak To has been characterized as one of the longest continuous battles fought by the U.S. Army in Vietnam. Contributing to the defeat of expert North Vietnamese Army units were U.S. superiority in the command and control of units, close and timely logistic support, the removal of enemy hiding places, and the imaginative use of new techniques and weapons.

CHAPTER VIII

Fire Support Base CROOK (June 1969)

Fire Support Surveillance Base FLOYD (August 1970)

A major innovation of the Vietnam War was the fire support base. Because there were no well-defined battle lines, fire support of maneuver units could not always be accomplished from secure, behind-the-line positions or from major base areas. Often, positions had to be secured in enemy-dominated territory.

By late 1966 the usual procedure was to establish fire support bases containing headquarters elements, medical facilities, and other support activities, as well as supporting light, medium, and sometimes heavy artillery. Setting up such bases became the routine opening phase of search operations. For example, the beginning of Operation JUNCTION CITY, 22 February–14 May 1967, included a drive by the 1st Infantry Division to open a road northward through War Zone C for the purpose of establishing fire support bases from which the maneuver battalions would operate and receive their artillery support.

These early bases were often attacked by North Vietnamese Army and Viet Cong forces, as they made ideal targets for enemy offensive actions. Eventually, because of the enemy's inclination to attack such installations, fire support bases were established for the express purpose of decoying the enemy. In these instances, sophisticated target detection means including radar, sensor devices, and infrared night sighting devices were used to give warning of the enemy's approach. This combination proved to be eminently successful, and large numbers of attacking enemy forces were destroyed in several such battles at little cost in friendly casualties. The decoy concept was further expanded to include the deployment of fire support bases to facilitate screening of suspected major enemy avenues of approach. This technique was employed extensively by the 25th Infantry Division during the later stages of its tenure in Vietnam.

FIRE SUPPORT BASE CROOK, *June 1969.*

The action of 5-8 June 1969 at Fire Support Base CROOK in Tay Ninh Province was a classic example of "offensive fire support base" techniques. Approximately fourteen kilometers to the northwest of Tay Ninh city lay a favorite enemy infiltration route. Close to the Cambodian border, the area was a major artery for enemy troops and supplies moving back and forth between War Zone C in the east and Cambodia in the west. In April 1969, Fire Support Base CROOK was established to prevent enemy movement along this route and to provide support for offensive operations in the vicinity. The plan assumed that the enemy would not be able to resist an attempt to knock out the isolated post.

Terrain surrounding the fire support base was flat and generally forested. To the east lay the triple-canopy jungle of War Zone C; to the southwest and west were abandoned rice paddies, while north of the base was scattered double-canopy jungle. Although observation and fields of fire were limited to 200 meters on the east, they ranged out to as much as 1,000 meters over the abandoned rice paddies.

Positioned inside the base was a small force of the 25th Infantry Division, consisting of Company B, 3d Battalion, 22d Infantry; Battery A, 7th Battalion, 11th Artillery, with six 105-mm. howitzers; and elements of the mortar, communications, and medical platoons of the 3d Battalion, 22d Infantry. U.S. planners hoped that the enemy would see Fire Support Base CROOK as an attractive prospect for one of their carefully planned night attacks. Though physically isolated, the base was far from alone. Supporting fire from artillery at other locations as well as from gunships and tactical air elements was arranged around the fire support base perimeter. Early warning was provided for by all available means, including the latest equipment such as sensors, radars, starlight scopes, and patrolling helicopters mounting xenon searchlights.

Preparation of the area surrounding Fire Support Base CROOK was extensive. Bulldozers cleared fields of fire, but isolated patches of concealment were deliberately left to attract North Vietnamese Army reconnaissance parties and observers. These patches were placed so that radar was able to cover them exactly, and direct 105-mm. howitzer fire was ready to destroy anyone using them. There were concentric circles, resembling race tracks, cut at 100–150 meters and 300 meters beyond the fighting positions. These circles were to deny the enemy's rocket propelled grenade gunners ideal firing positions and to increase the effectiveness of U.S. supporting fire. From the air, observers used the circles as a range scale, reducing the chance of error and providing common frames of reference between the observers and the defenders.

The situation at Fire Support Base CROOK remained relatively quiet until the evening of June 5, when the seismic sensors picked up heavy enemy activity less than one kilometer to the northwest. In addition, radar detected small groups moving in the wood lines around the base. Artillery was fired at these areas and, as apprehension of an impending attack grew, the officer in command, Major Joseph E. Hacia, executive officer of the 3d Battalion, 22d Infantry, ordered interdicting fire from supporting artillery on trails, road junctions, and likely assembly areas. Despite the artillery fire, enemy activity continued, and by midevening, Major Hacia had ordered a 100-percent alert. At 0255 hours, a barrage by 107-mm. and 122-mm. rockets, 75-mm. recoilless rifles, rocket propelled grenades, and 60-mm. and 82-mm. mortar fire was directed at the base. Fortunately, most of the rocket fire went over the base, but mortar rounds hit in and around the perimeter, killing one U.S. soldier. Otherwise, damage was slight.

Co-ordinated with the attack by fire, the enemy launched a battalion-size ground attack from the south and west, which was met by a heavy volume of grazing fire from the defenders. The artillery battery within the base went into action with a close fire support technique referred to as "killer junior." This technique provided light artillery fire to a depth of 150 to 200 meters around the base, while medium and heavy supporting artillery hit suspected enemy positions throughout the area. On the perimeter, a sixteen-man enemy force did succeed in breaking through the wire with bangalore torpedoes, but it was stopped by riflemen in the bunkers.

By 0400 hours, the full gamut of air support, including tactical air fighters and gunships of all kinds, went into action over the battle area, hitting suspected enemy rocket and mortar positions and covering all the open areas around the base with fire. Some fifteen enemy .51-caliber antiaircraft machine guns were reported in action, but they were suppressed by the gunships.

Wilting under the heavy supporting fire, the enemy withdrew into the jungle, and by 0530 the base was receiving only light, sporadic fire. Tactical air and artillery fire continued to pound away at the withdrawing enemy, in an effort to restrict his movement and inflict additional casualties. At first light, B Company moved out of the base on a sweep which uncovered seventy-six enemy bodies and fifteen small arms, plus a variety of ammunition, documents, and extraneous gear.

The next evening enemy activity resumed in almost the same pattern. First, the seismic sensor equipment and radars picked up heavy movement, this time to the northwest and east of the base; then radars began detecting three- to five-man groups moving in the wood lines. All return fire was made with artillery and mortars, including the base's artillery battery, which engaged in direct fire. Although all detectable movement had ceased by 0100 hours, the artillery continued firing "killer junior."

At 0200 hours, a Nighthawk helicopter with a xenon searchlight spotted large groups of enemy troops moving toward the base along the road from the east. Shortly after the artillery shifted and began pounding these new targets, the base was hit with intense enemy preparatory fire followed by simultaneous ground attacks by battalion-size forces from the northeast and northwest. Again the base suffered minimal damage, and only three men were wounded.

Army and Air Force gunships, including the Nighthawk helicopter and AC-119 and AC-47 fixed-wing aircraft, engaged the attacking enemy forces under illumination to the northeast and northwest. Additional helicopter gunships suppressed the enemy's .51-caliber antiaircraft guns firing from the west. Available artillery and mortar fire engaged the enemy's supporting positions to the east and south. All this firing, along with intense small arms, automatic weapons, and direct artillery fire from the base itself, wreaked havoc with the attacking enemy battalions.

Despite the volume of defensive fire, the northwestern attacking battalion succeeded in breaching the outer wire before it was stopped. However, the northeastern assault was stopped short of the wire. Most of the attacking force were trapped and cut down in the open as they attempted to withdraw, and by 0530 enemy troops that were able to do so had retreated into the jungle. A sweep of the area on the morning of the third day, 7 June, yielded 323 enemy bodies, 10 prisoners, and over 40 weapons, including two machine guns and two mortars, plus a large quantity of documents, ammunition, and equipment. The following evening the base received light small arms and mortar fire, which caused no casualties. There was no ground attack. In general, this last attack seemed little more than a parting gesture from the badly beaten 272d Viet Cong Regiment.

A total disaster for the enemy, Fire Support Base CROOK was another example of the ability to defeat the North Vietnamese Army and Viet Cong during one of their classic offensive operations. The battle demonstrated the rapid building of a fire base, the use of modern detection equipment, and the integration of the full spectrum of modern fire support techniques to achieve a decisive victory.

Later in the Vietnam conflict, another generation of fire support bases was developed. Fire Support Surveillance Base FLOYD was conceived by the 173d Airborne Brigade as a total interdiction base covering an entire valley floor. The base properly integrated sensors, radar, and other target acquisition means with the system of direct and indirect fire support. Fire base facilities were organized to enable rapid reaction to confirmed targets and to provide adequate base defense. (*Diagram 2*) The nerve center of the base was the tactical operations center, in which radar and optical scopes and monitoring devices were located. Installing the target acquisition means nearby insured rapid comparison of readouts and confirmation of targets. The mortar fire direction centers were also located in the tactical operations center in order to disseminate target information more efficiently to the indirect fire weapons.

Successful implementation of this fire base concept took place shortly before daylight on 29 August 1970. The 3d Battalion, 2d North Vietnamese Army Regiment, entered a valley in northern Binh Dinh Province from the south and marched openly along the road toward the area of Hoai An District, where they were to occupy mountain base camps and conduct operations against district forces while replenishing their supply of rice. As the enemy column entered the valley, the southernmost sensor was activated, continuing for twenty minutes. A sweep by the PPS-5 radar confirmed that an enemy column was moving north in the valley. The decision was made to engage the rear of the column in the hope of getting a second try at its head. The rear was hit with mortar fire and, as hoped, the

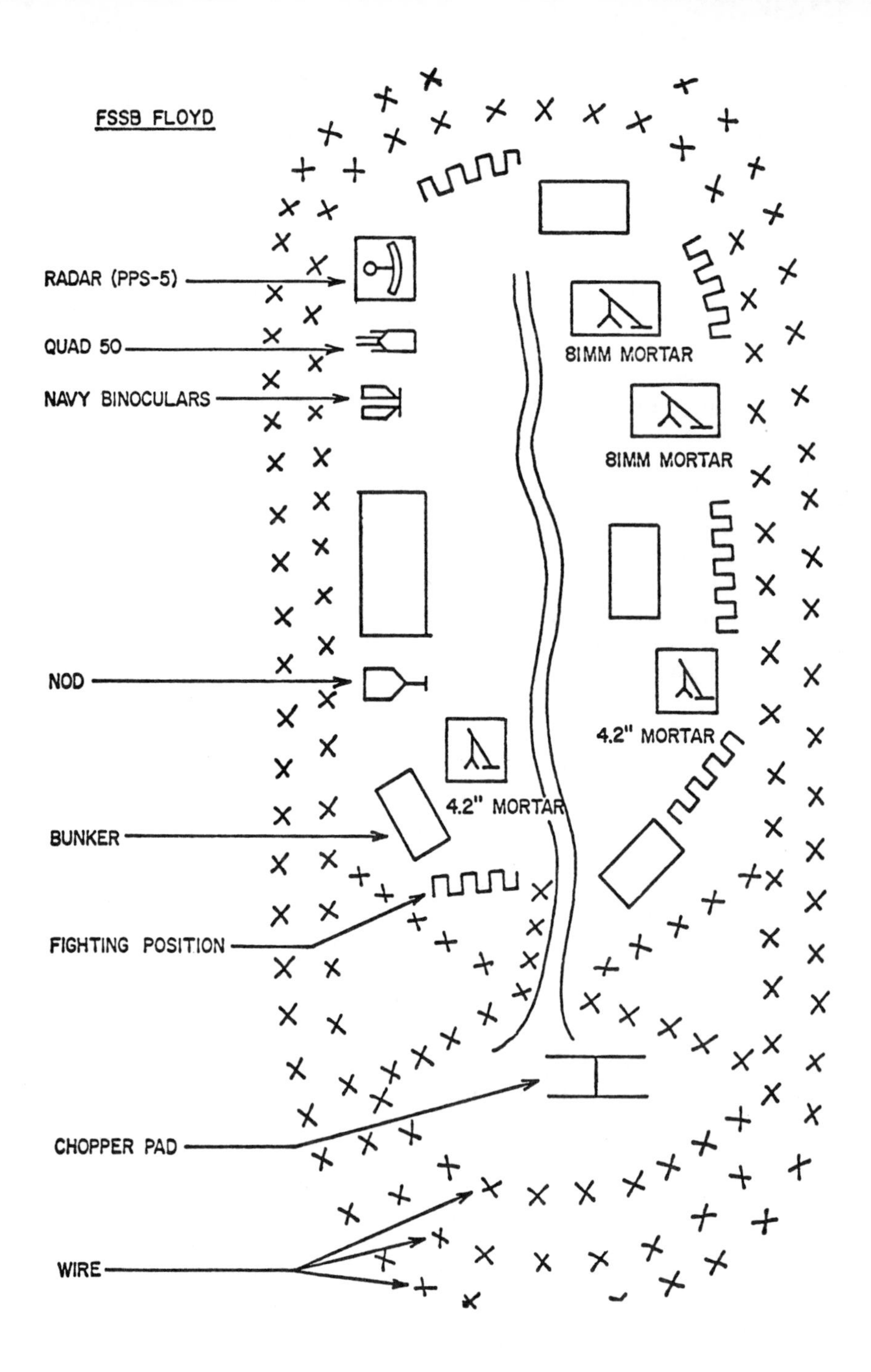

Diagram 2. Fire Support Surveillance Base FLOYD layout, 29 August 1970.

remainder of the column marched on. The radar continued to track the enemy, and additional sensors became active. By this time night observation devices had picked up enemy activity. When the head of the column activated a sensor, it was hit by fire from 105-mm. howitzers, 4.2-inch mortars, and 81-mm. mortars. After this barrage, the PPS-5 and night observation devices confirmed that the enemy was fleeing to the west. Quad .50-caliber machine gun fire pursued the retreating enemy, and mortar fire blocked his escape to the west. Contact was not lost until the enemy left the killing zone.

At first light, a reaction force from the 173d Airborne Brigade began a sweep of the valley floor. Blood trails leading west into the high ground confirmed the accuracy of the barrages. The enemy had not been able to remove all of his dead and wounded. Reconnaissance forces found six dead enemy soldiers and one wounded, along with one AK-50, one 60-mm. mortar, and numerous pieces of individual equipment that had been discarded. On 3 September a wounded enemy soldier, captured in the mountains near the 506 Valley, confirmed that the toll of dead and wounded had been great.

The exact results of the action will probably never be known; however, because of the damage done, the 3d Battalion, 2d North Vietnamese Army Regiment, avoided significant contact with allied forces for several months. The results were substantial considering there was no close contact between infantry units.

Fire Support Surveillance Base FLOYD represented an economy-of-force measure employing a target acquisition system and immediate fire support in an interdiction mission. The terms "killer junior" and "killer senior" referred to direct fire defensive programs of the field artillery. Both techniques were designed to defend fire bases against enemy ground attack and used mechanical, time-fuzed projectiles set to burst approximately thirty feet off the ground at ranges of 100 to 1000 meters. The name "killer junior" applied to light and medium artillery (105-mm. and 155-mm.), while "killer senior" referred to the same system using eight-inch howitzers. This technique proved more effective in many instances than direct fire with "beehive" ammunition, because the enemy could avoid the beehive ammunition by lying prone or crawling. For example, in October 1967 during the battle of Xa Cat, which involved an attack by several enemy battalions on the 1st Infantry Division's Fire Base CAISSON VI, artillery firing beehive ammunition had little effect on attacking enemy troops, because they approached the perimeter by crawling. However, a switch to time-fuzed explosives stopped the advance. Another successful application of the "killer" technique was in clearing snipers from around base areas.

In building Fire Support Base CROOK, many of the rapid construction techniques which had been developed during the previous months, while positioning divisional patrol bases along the Cambodian border, were used. Construction usually started early in the day and proceeded according to the following steps. The exact position of the fire support base was selected and an engineer stake was driven at the center. A rope forty meters long was attached to the stake and stretched out from the center, forming the radius of the base and establishing the location of the bunker line. Next, an aiming circle was positioned at the center and a stake was driven at 0° to mark the location of the first bunker. Additional stakes were driven every 15° around the perimeter to mark the location of all twenty-four bunkers, which had been established as the ideal number for a rifle company. Another circle was marked seventy-five meters out from the bunker line, thus establishing the location of the defensive wire barrier.

After the bunker positions had been marked, a standard package was dropped at each of the twenty-four stakes by a helicopter. This package contained one fifteen-pound, shaped demolition charge; two sheets of pierced steel planking; and a bundle of sandbags. The shaped charges were placed next to the engineer stakes, and the initial hole for the bunker was blown. A standard nine-foot bunker was then built by using the pierced steel planking and sandbags and by squaring up the blown crater.

While the fighting bunkers were being constructed, bulldozers were busily digging holes for larger command and control bunkers inside the perimeter. The berms were pushed up for artillery firing positions and later between the bunkers on the outer perimeter. The wire barrier was established using one row of triple concertina wire. The area between the bunker line and the wire barrier was then laced with claymore mines. The fire support base was completed when a Chinook helicopter flew in with a fully assembled, twenty-foot observation tower. Time of construction varied, but in each case the company defending the base was dug in with complete overhead cover by nightfall of the first day.

The fights at Fire Support Base CROOK and Fire Support Surveillance Base FLOYD demonstrated the successful integration of sensor devices to provide early warning and identification of enemy units. These devices were positioned either through the air or by hand and could detect the movement of humans within a range of about 40 meters and of vehicles within 300 meters.

Other target acquisition devices used successfully at Fire Support Base CROOK and Fire Support Surveillance Base FLOYD were the ground surveillance radars and the night observation devices. The radar sets organic to division maneuver battalions were used primarily to provide short- and medium-range identification and location of enemy targets during periods of limited visibility. The AN/PPS-5 radar had a maximum range of 5 kilometers and the AN/PPS-4 radar

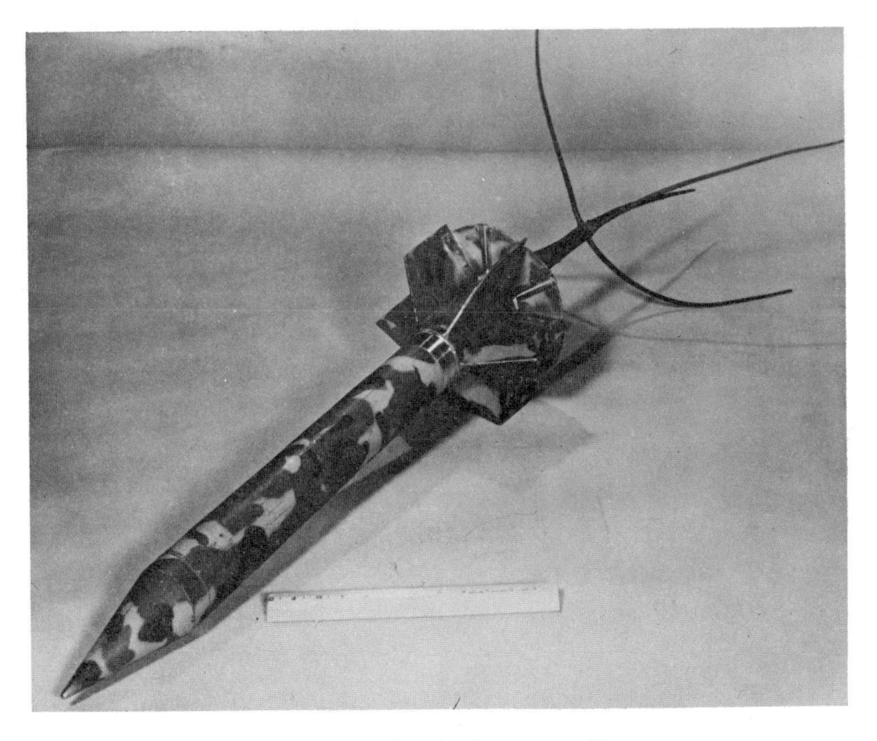

AERIAL DELIVERED SEISMIC INTRUSION DETECTOR

had a 1.5-kilometer range for personnel detection. Both were used to protect the night defensive positions. Along with radar there were the night observation devices, either the older infrared lights or the newer starlight scopes. These scopes intensified the available light rather than emitting a light source of their own. The new sensors were of limited value in themselves, but when properly integrated into an over-all surveillance and target acquisition plan, as at Fire Support Base CROOK and Fire Support Surveillance Base FLOYD, they were most effective.

A final innovation was the artillery ambush, a technique developed by the 1st Battalion, 77th Artillery, 1st Cavalry Division Artillery. The ambush involved the covert planning of a homemade trip flare device with the trip wire running across the road. A fire unit was laid on this grid and fired on the flare signal. Two flares of different colors could be used to determine the direction of travel of the target unit. Later, with the arrival of the modern sensor devices, the technique was further refined.

In conclusion, the unique employment of the fire support bases in Vietnam can be considered an innovation. The use of these bases to

Starlight Scope, Rifle-Mounted Night Observation Device

invite enemy attacks, the placement of the bases, the techniques of co-ordinating supporting fire, and the co-ordination of target acquisition means were prime examples of the integration of various methods and the use of new equipment to destroy the enemy.

CHAPTER IX

Tam Ky
(March 1968)

In early 1968, elements of the 23d Infantry Division (Americal) fought a sharp, decisive battle near the village of Tam Ky in Quang Tin Province. This action demonstrates the use of armored cavalry in the Vietnam War. The cavalry role was expanded, particularly in conjunction with air scouts, and armored vehicle doctrine was modified to suit the Vietnam environment.

A good example of the armored cavalry in Vietnam is the operation of the 1st Squadron, 1st Cavalry, 23d Infantry Division, at Tam Ky. The squadron included three armored cavalry troops plus an air cavalry troop, Troop C, 7th Squadron, 17th Cavalry. (This unit had just returned from an operation in the Pineapple Forest west of Tam Ky.) At the time, the division was using Lieutenant Colonel Walter C. "Mike" Cousland's cavalry squadron as a separate maneuver battalion under division control in his own area of operations against the 72d Local Force Battalion, the 70th Main Force Battalion, and the V-13 and V-15 Local Force Companies. On the evening of 3 March 1968, the squadron, minus two cavalry platoons, was at its base camp on Hawk Hill. The 1st Platoon of Troop A was on Hill 10, securing a sector of Route 1; the 2d Platoon of Troop A was at Tam Ky, prepared to assist in the defense of the province headquarters. Earlier in the day, Captain Michael B. Prothero had assumed command of Troop C. Little did he realize that in less than twenty-four hours he would be commanding his troop and a rifle company against a North Vietnamese Army regiment.

Captain George R. Kaczor, the squadron's S-2 (officer in charge of the military intelligence section), was busily studying his intelligence reports. Major Wade E. Medbery, Jr., the S-3 (officer in charge of the operations and training section), had issued Colonel Cousland's orders for the next day. In the tactical operations center, all was quiet with the exception of an occasional periodic situation report. Suddenly the silence of the evening was broken by a loud explosion followed by a heavy bombardment of forty-five rounds of 122-

mm. rockets and fifty rounds of mortar fire. Apparently the enemy was close by and in considerable strength.

At first light the air cavalry discovered the rocket-firing positions on Hill 34 to the west of the base camp. The commanding general extended the cavalry's area of operations to the west and attached one company of infantry. The squadron was again to be committed as a maneuver battalion to eliminate the enemy force that had fired on it. Troop C was ordered to move to the west to link up with Company A, 3d Battalion, 21st Infantry. About that time, fifteen North Vietnamese soldiers were sighted in bunkers, and the S-3 requested an immediate air strike. At 0938 hours, Troop C started moving toward the area of contact as the air cavalry discovered more and more enemy positions. Some small arms fire was being received by the aircraft, and one Huey was hit but continued to fly. The forward air controller arrived on station and asked the air cavalry to mark the target area. Fighters completed the first air strike at 1100 hours.

The linkup of the infantry company and Troop C was completed shortly after noon. Colonel Cousland designated the cavalry troop's leader as the team commander and gave him operational control of the air cavalry in the area of contact. The enemy was defending from well-fortified positions. Throughout the afternoon the cavalry-infantry team tested the enemy's positions, pulling back periodically to let the fighters strike. Finally, the North Vietnamese could take no more. As they began to withdraw, the last air strikes and the artillery took a heavy toll.

At 1920 Troop C and Company A, 3d Battalion, 21st Infantry, moved to a night defensive position on Hill 34—the same hill from which the enemy rockets had been fired a few hours earlier. Hill 34 was triangular in shape, with rice paddies and streams on two of its three sides; it was an excellent defensive position. The field of fire over the rice paddies was well suited to the long-range, direct fire weapons on the tanks and armored cavalry assault vehicles. This position guarded the Phu Xuan River, a known enemy route, allowed observation of the enemy position, and prevented the enemy from using the same firing data against Hawk Hill as was used the previous night.

Captain Prothero closed his units into the night location at 2012 hours. It had been a hard day for the cavalrymen and infantrymen, but the task of preparing the night defense was vitally important. The men learned that they were dealing with the 3d Regiment of the 3d North Vietnamese Army Division. The enemy had originally intended to attack Hawk Hill, but Captain Prothero's force had thwarted his efforts. While Colonel Cousland and his staff planned the next day's operation, the troops started working on their defenses. The general

ARMORED CAVALRY ASSAULT VEHICLES WITH RPG SCREENS ON FRONT

trace of the position resembled the old wagon train coils of the Indian wars on the American plains.

The armored vehicles themselves provided protection against the enemy's small arms and automatic weapons, but the men added a new device to protect the vehicles against the armor-piercing B40 rocket-propelled grenade (RPG). It was called the RPG screen. Nothing more than a section of "cyclone" fence, it caused a shaped-charge warhead to detonate before it hit the vehicle. Each crew set up a section of fence in front of its position, and the command element in the center established a second screen around its vehicles. This simple expedient saved many vehicles and bunker positions.

Fighting positions were built between each cavalry vehicle, and some of the M60 machine guns on the armored cavalry assault vehicles were dismounted and positioned to provide grazing fire. Each vehicle carried three or four rolls of concertina barbed wire. The wire was strung as an outer barrier. Finally, four or five claymore mines were set up in front of each armored vehicle. Listening posts were sent out, and Team C waited for the enemy.

Except for a few rounds which landed about 100 meters outside the perimeter at 2255 hours, the 3d North Vietnamese Army Regiment let the team alone that night. During this lull, Colonel Cousland analyzed his situation and prepared for the next day. He decided to send Troop C and Company A back into the area of contact in the morning and to attack the suspected enemy positions from the rear.

ARMORED PERSONNEL CARRIERS CLEAR THE WAY AS INFANTRY FOLLOWS *using vehicles for cover.*

Two previously planned air strikes were made on the area shortly after first light, followed by an artillery preparation. After an aerial resupply of ammunition, the cavalry-infantry team moved out with air cavalry elements on either flank. At 1305 hours the team received small arms and automatic weapons fire at a range of fifty meters. This attack soon developed into a heavy fight which lasted until 1830 hours, when the unit withdrew to its night defensive positions.

On the third day Colonel Cousland committed Troop B; Troop C, Company A of the 3d Battalion, 21st Infantry; and the air cavalry troop. The battle lasted for several more days and resulted in 436 North Vietnamese soldiers killed and many weapons captured. The 3d North Vietnamese Army Regiment ceased to exist as an effective fighting force.

Much of the battle of Tam Ky was fought by the armored vehicles of the cavalry squadron. The M48 had been the standard medium tank since 1956, but its sister vehicle in the battle, the armored cavalry assault vehicle, was modified specifically for the cavalry squadrons in Vietnam. The old machine gun "jeep" had lacked cross-country mobility and armor protection for the crew. Although the M114 had been used for a while as the scout vehicle, it was replaced with the much more reliable armored cavalry assault vehicle (ACAV).

The ACAV was actually an M113 personnel carrier modified by the addition of an armament subsystem. This "A" kit consisted of hatch armor, a shield for the commander's .50-caliber machine gun, two elbow pintle mounts with gun shields for mounting M60 machine guns on both sides of the M113, and a removable pintle mount on the rear as an alternate mount for one of the M60's. The armored cavalry assault vehicle originated with the 11th Armored Cavalry, which equipped its M113's with the armament subsystems before arriving in Vietnam. The idea soon spread through all units in Vietnam. A "B" kit armament subsystem was also developed. It consisted of hatch armor and a shield for the commander's .50-caliber machine gun. This kit was used on the cavalry mortar carriers.

One of the major innovations in the employment of armor in Vietnam was the use of the M113 as a fighting vehicle. In addition to being used to transport troops to a battle area, it was employed like a light tank, using the fire from mounted weapons to destroy the enemy in close combat. The infantrymen rode on or in the carrier until contact with the enemy was made, then they dismounted. Carriers led the assaults, clearing paths through the underbrush as they went. In many cases, particularly in dense foliage and mine-infested terrain, the infantry troops did better to remain mounted and assault the objective as the carriers detonated antipersonnel mines and booby traps. Most of the personnel carriers, which were used as assault vehicles, were modified as armored cavalry assault vehicles. This technique was discussed by Major General John J. Tolson, III, Commanding General, 1st Cavalry Division (Airmobile).

> [The APC's] didn't have the 90mm guns as did the tanks, but they had the APC's armor protection for the personnel. Their 50 cals. were still a great help in going into the fortified positions. Actually, on occasions, we used the APC platoons very similar to the tank platoons.

The tanks which fought in the battle of Tam Ky in March 1968 were M48A2's. Although their firepower, armor, and maneuverability endeared them to the tanker, their weight and bulk was often more than was needed. The M551 "General Sheridan" armored reconnaissance airborne assault vehicle had been under development as "a lightweight armored vehicle to support ground reconnaissance." In mid-1969 it began to replace some of the tanks in the armored cavalry squadrons.

The relatively large 152-mm. gun and launcher fired combustible-case conventional ammunition. It could also fire the Shillelagh missile but was not used for this purpose in Vietnam. The gun was superior to the 90-mm. tank gun against both bunkers and personnel, and its canister round was excellent to open up bamboo thickets. A disadvantage of the M551 was its limited ability to "bust" through dense jungle. The main battle tank was greatly superior in this respect.

In phasing in the General Sheridans, the 11th Armored Cavalry was issued three Sheridans for two of the ACAV's in the reconnaissance platoon. Thus, the cavalry troop lost none of its jungle-busting ability and greatly increased its firepower. In the division's cavalry squadrons, however, tanks had been assigned to each cavalry platoon instead of to a separate tank troop. The Sheridan was substituted on a one-for-one basis for M48 tanks, resulting in a loss of jungle-busting ability.

An excellent example of the Sheridan's fighting capabilities occurred on 11 March 1969, almost a year after the battle of Tam Ky, when Captain John W. Wells, III, moved Troop A, 3d Squadron, 4th Cavalry, into a night defensive position. He was located at a road junction west of the Ben Cui Rubber Plantation along a known enemy infiltration route. Judging from the results, the enemy did not realize the unit was there. All of the Sheridans in the perimeter were equipped with night observation devices. One of the crews detected a group of enemy troops in an open field, moving directly toward it. Captain Wells instructed the crew to hold its fire and load its canisters. He then moved to the Sheridan to observe the enemy movement personally. As the enemy came closer, the large number of radios indicated that this unit was the command group of a North Vietnamese battalion.

When Captain Wells gave the order to fire, the first round eliminated the whole command group. Having lost its leadership, the enemy soldiers panicked and milled around in the area. In a few minutes the enemy lost forty-two men killed in action and one prisoner of war as compared to two U.S. soldiers wounded. This encounter demonstrated that the Sheridan was a significant combat weapon even during hours of darkness.

Frequently, tanks from the division tank battalion were attached to the cavalry squadron when additional jungle-busting power was needed. Another solution to the problem was to attach one or two combat engineer vehicles (CEV), M728, to the squadron for certain operations. The need for a combat engineer vehicle first arose during World War II in the hedgerows of Normandy, when bulldozer blades were fitted to tanks, but it was not until Vietnam that such a vehicle arrived on the battlefield. The M728 had been designed to support armor and mechanized units through fire-swept areas and to accomplish a broad range of combat engineering tasks. It was assigned to the division engineer battalions. The combat engineer vehicle is a

"GENERAL SHERIDAN" ARMORED RECONNAISSANCE AIRBORNE ASSAULT VEHICLE

modified M60 tank with a bulldozer blade, a turret-mounted A-frame and winch, and a 165-mm. demolition gun. With its armor protection, this vehicle could move forward under enemy fire to destroy obstacles and fortifications with its demolition gun, clear obstacles with its bulldozer blade, and use the A-frame to lift equipment or place and recover bridges.

In the 23d Infantry Division (Americal), the combat engineer vehicle repeatedly proved to be a valuable asset to engineer and infantry operations. The vehicle was used in fire support, base security, counterambush fire, direct assault of fortified positions, and limited reconnaissance by fire. It even spearheaded an infantry-cavalry charge in the village of Tap An Bac on 19 June 1969, when division elements came to the defense of two bulldozers and a work party from the 26th Engineer Battalion. The day-long fight was won in the final assault.

The M48 tank saw combat for the first time in Vietnam. For the most part, tanks were part of a tank-infantry or cavalry team and conventional tactics were used. Commanders did, however, seek better ways to use their limited armor assets.

In December 1966, the 2d Battalion, 34th Armor, was assigned to secure the route from Tay Ninh to Tri Tam, where small groups of Viet Cong had been successfully mining the road. The battalion commander chose to use the "thunder run" technique to offset this enemy action. During the hours of darkness, a tank company or platoon "ran

COMBAT ENGINEER VEHICLE

the road" two or three times at irregular intervals. It fired canisters and .50-caliber and 7.62-mm. machine guns at likely enemy locations on both sides of the road. After three nights, mining incidents stopped, and the first *Chieu Hoi* rallier surrendered. He attributed his action to the thunder runs. This technique was used by most of the tank units in Vietnam.

Lieutenant General William R. Peers, Commanding General, I Field Force, Vietnam, made the following comment about tanks.

> In the southern coastal provinces . . . the monsoon rains are sufficiently light that normally tanks can operate the year round. Here they proved most productive. For example, the provisional U.S. tank platoon in the Phan Thiet area has added more stability to the area than any other single element. Having been successful in blasting the enemy out of their positions on numerous occasions, they have given a high degree of confidence to the ARVN, the RF/PF, and the local population. On the other hand, they are greatly feared by the enemy to the extent that he has tried on numerous occasions, but without success, to destroy or otherwise eliminate them.

The shock effect of even a single tank in guerrilla warfare was apparent in Vietnam. Lieutenant Colonel Ronald J. Fairfield, Commanding Officer, 1st Battalion, 69th Armor, stated, "The NVA/VC have shown a reluctance to engage tanks where they can be avoided." A year later, Lieutenant Colonel Paul S. Williams, Jr., while commanding the same battalion, said: "Captured documents and interrogation reports disclose that the enemy is afraid of tanks. We feel what he really fears is the cannister round and its effect. This [feeling] has been justified, to a degree, by the absence of contact when tank and infantry units move together." Obviously, the enemy did fight armored and cavalry units, but usually he either was put in a position where he had to fight or felt that he possessed sufficient strength to defeat the American force. Colonel Donn A. Starry, one of the commanders of the 11th Armored Cavalry, stated, "A cavalry troop well handled was generally capable of fighting anything the NVA could field, at least until additional cavalry and firepower could be mustered."

An example of the cavalry's shock action occurred when the U.S. 1st Infantry Division staged the battle of Minh Thanh road. The division leaked word that it planned to move engineer equipment and supply vehicles between Minh Thanh and An Loc on 9 July 1966. Actually, two armored cavalry troops and one infantry company were sent along the route, and other combat and combat support forces were positioned to assist. When the 272d North Vietnamese Army Regiment spotted the cavalry force from its ambush positions, it attacked. By the time the smoke cleared the enemy regiment had lost 239 dead on the battlefield, 89 captured, and an estimated 304 killed but not visible in the area. The regiment was probably reduced to less than 50 percent of its strength.

Some of the findings of the official "Evaluation of Mechanized and Armor Combat Operations in Vietnam (MACOV)" summarize the effectiveness of armored cavalry units.

> Armored cavalry units were employed in roles previously assigned to tank and infantry maneuver battalions in addition to the traditional reconnaissance, security, and economy of force roles. This change has evolved due to the nature of the enemy in Vietnam, the concept of area war and the balanced combined arms structure of the armored cavalry squadron. There are definitive battlefields in the traditional sense, the enemy has a propensity for avoiding contact by moving in small groups—massing only for short term offensive actions. Armored cavalry squadrons have proven effective not only as a force to find and fix the enemy, but also as an aggressive offensive force. The balanced combined arms of structure and inherent capability for quick response and extended independent action have made it possible to employ the armored cavalry squadron as a well-balanced maneuver battalion.

The most important materiel innovations associated with mechanized warfare in Vietnam were the combat engineer vehicles, the M551 General Sheridans, and the modifications of the M113 personnel carrier. These vehicles were integrated with new techniques, such as airmobile tactics, secure communications, and night vision equipment, and proved enormously effective. The rocket-propelled grenade screen was one of the most widely used innovations of the war. Cyclone fence could be found at virtually every U.S. installation in Vietnam. The concept of detonating enemy rocket-propelled grenades before they hit the target was sound, and the adaptation of existing materiel for this use was ingenious.

The use of the M113 in a tank-like role will interest the military theorists for years. The M113 brought to the Vietnam battlefield the shock, firepower, and mobility that are characteristic of tank warfare. The terrain was less than ideal for tanks; the enemy's forces included no significant armor formations. Given these conditions, it is not surprising that the M113 was often used as a tank.

The development of jungle-busting techniques and thunder runs was the logical outgrowth of mechanized forces in the Vietnam environment. Every combat commander in Vietnam faced the problems of jungle warfare and enemy mines. Jungle-busting was the only way to exploit mechanized mobility in the forests, and the firepower and shock action of an M113 or a General Sheridan was invaluable to a force in an occupied enemy base camp.

U.S. armor and mechanized formations made a significant contribution to the allied effort in Vietnam. The armor soldier with modern equipment, training, and leadership proved his effectiveness and gave the Viet Cong and North Vietnamese Army ample reason to avoid tanks where they could.

CHAPTER X

Phong Cao
(November 1966)

The battle of Phong Cao was a classic encirclement operation that illustrates a succession of innovations widely used in Vietnam. Infantry tactical formations and counterguerrilla techniques aided by the ever-present helicopter were immensely successful. The battle began on 6 November 1966 when the 2d Battalion (Airborne), 502d Infantry, reinforced with the local Civilian Irregular Defense Group, air-assaulted into four landing zones in the jungle fifteen miles northwest of Tuy Hoa. The Strike Force was one of three battalions assigned to the 1st Brigade, 101st Airborne Division, and was commanded by Lieutenant Colonel Frank L. Dietrich. Colonel Dietrich was no newcomer to combat; he had fought in World War II from Africa to the Rhine with the 504th Parachute Infantry Regiment.

The Strike Force was stalking the 5th Battalion, 95th North Vietnamese Regiment. The enemy was conducting training operations while waiting for ammunition being brought in from Binh Dinh and for replacements coming from North Vietnam. Only 214 of the enemy's 320 authorized officers and men were on duty. Their training area included a complex of base camps in a saddle formed by Hills 450 in the north and 350 in the south. The enemy battalion was to engage any small unit patrols that entered the training area, but if a large U.S. force moved in, it planned to slip out and wait for its ammunition and replacements at another site.

Colonel Dietrich, at the time of the Strike Force's air assault, did not have the details of the enemy's mission or situation, but he did know that a long-range patrol had spotted an unoccupied base camp on Hill 450 a month before. During this period in the war, long-range patrols were being used more frequently and were becoming a major source of intelligence. Intelligence indicated that an enemy division headquarters and elements of the 95th Regiment were in the area. Colonel Dietrich reasoned that the enemy was occupying positions on Hill 450. He also suspected that the North Vietnamese Army forces would avoid combat and leave the area if they realized that the Strike Force's objective was the hill. To conceal his battalion's target,

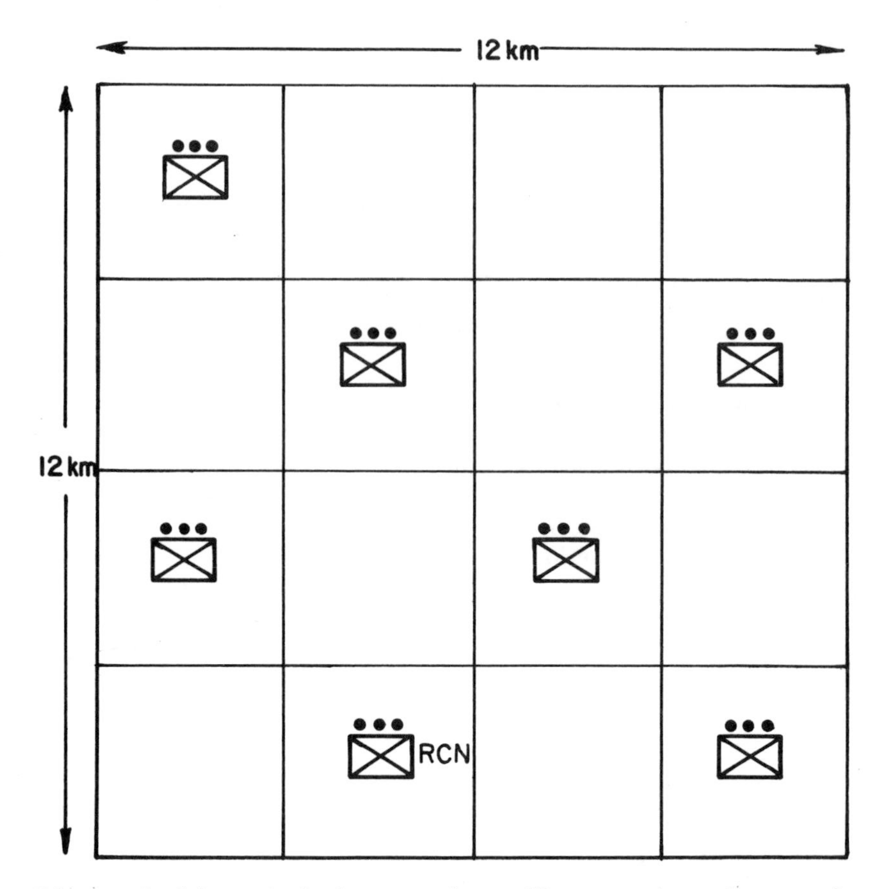

Diagram 3. Schematic deployment of two rifle companies and reconnaissance platoon in checkerboard search pattern. (Drawing is only representative as no attempt is made to arrive at exact configuration in practice.)

therefore, he selected a deception objective west of Hill 450. He chose landing zones around the decoy area and instructed his company commanders to move initially in a direction that would lead the North Vietnamese commander to believe that Hill 450 would not be searched.

As the operation began, the helicopter assaults were unopposed, and the companies moved out in modified checkerboard formation. The checkerboard, a method of searching an area by covering alternate squares with small units, was a new technique created by Lieutenant Colonel Henry E. "Hank" Emerson, who had preceded Colonel Dietrich as the commander of 2d Battalion (Airborne), 502d Infantry. (*Diagram 3*)

Company B made the first contact with four Viet Cong, killing one. The Recondos, the battalion's reconnaissance platoon reinforced to fifty-man strength, killed a lone Viet Cong in the only other encounter of the day. The 7th and 8th of November brought light contact, and by early afternoon of the 8th, the battalion had turned from the deception objective and was heading east. At 1830, elements of the Recondo Platoon reached Hill 450 and spotted four North Vietnamese in a company-size base camp. In the failing light the enemy had not seen the Recondos. The battalion commander was immediately informed of the Recondos' contact and, during the night of 8–9 November, his idea for surrounding the saddle was passed to the Strike Force commanders. Elements of Company B would attack from the west, while the rest of the company established a blocking position in the south. Company C, commanded by Captain Stephen Silvasy, Jr., would make a forced march into blocking positions in the southeast quadrant. Company A, commanded by Captain "Mike" McFadden, would be lifted by helicopter to the northeast quadrant. The Recondos would close the circle in the north between Companies A and B.

At 1000 the following morning, the Recondo Platoon was moving into position deployed as two sections. The two elements were separated by several hundred meters when Section A, led by platoon sergeant Richard F. Clemons, engaged first a trailwatcher and later an enemy platoon. The Recondos returned fire and were soon reinforced by the 2d Platoon from Company B, led by 1st Lieutenant Alden J. Holborn. Together the two units moved thirty meters up the wooded, vine-matted slope before enemy automatic weapons fire stopped their advance. As the fight was developing, the 3d Platoon of Company B, led by 1st Lieutenant John A. Marshok, Jr., had started to move north to come in behind the enemy. Lieutenant Marshok had been told that the battle was on the western slope of Hill 450, but his platoon was still well south of the hill when he became convinced that the sounds of the firefight were southwest of his position. Marshok reported the situation to his company commander and began to move west and then south to come in behind the enemy. The echo of the firefight in the mountains, the difficulty of reading the map in dense jungle, and the steep, slick slopes combined, however, to bring the platoon in on the southern flank of the Recondo-2d Platoon position.

At noon the Strike Force command post had the following information on the locations of the rifle companies. The main part of Company B was in a blocking position south of Hill 350. Company C was moving toward the southeast quadrant of Hill 350 but was still five hours away. Company A, several kilometers southeast of the battle, was approaching the area where it would be picked up for a helicopter assault to its place in the encirclement. Half of the Recondo

Platoon was in a blocking position north of Hill 450. The other half, Section A, was with the 2d Platoon of Company B in contact with an enemy platoon somewhere on the western slope of the saddle formed by Hills 450 and 350. Their location had been reported as the western slope of 450. The 3d Platoon of Company B had been moving north toward Hill 450. The platoon reported its position as a kilometer south of the hill, but it also stated that it could hear the Recondo fire-fight south of its location and that it was moving toward the sounds of the firing.

The 2d Battalion (Airborne), 502d Infantry, was normally supported by a command and control helicopter, but Colonel Dietrich had not used it since the day of the assault into Phong Cao. This stratagem was part of his deception plan to minimize the evidence that a U.S. battalion was in the area. Now, however, he called for the helicopter, and at 1225 it reported to his command post. Colonel Dietrich immediately took to the air, and the platoons in the jungle below identified their locations by displaying panels and dispensing colored smoke grenades. In a matter of minutes he understood the confusion of reports he had received from the Recondo section and the two platoons. The firefight was on the western slope of Hill 350. (*Diagram 4*) The three platoons were together now, and he directed them to pull back to allow an air strike on the enemy position.

By 1440 the platoons had disengaged, and two U.S. Air Force fighters made a pass over the enemy. Their bombs landed in the target area but fragments sprayed the U.S. platoons. Although there were no casualties, the air strike was canceled. In place of the fighters, a helicopter light fire team was deployed. As the gunships completed their strike, a battery of 155-mm. howitzers from the 1st Battalion, 30th Artillery, took up the fire. The artillery firing, which lasted over an hour, was followed by an assault of Company B's platoons. Enemy resistance to the assault was light, and as darkness fell on 9 November, two platoons of Company B were dug in on Hill 350. Company A's air assault had been unopposed, and except for the platoons on Hill 350, the battalion was in a blocking position around the saddle. There was a gap between the Recondos and Company A and another between the two Recondo sections. Claymores were positioned to fill the gap in the Recondo line. The battlefield was illuminated by 81-mm. mortars. A U.S. Air Force C-47 was on its way to replace the mortar illumination with flares. The encirclement was complete.

There was no contact during the night, but by 0715 on the morning of the 10th, the enemy had dispatched reconnaissance parties to determine U.S. locations. At 0840 a North Vietnamese reconnaissance patrol probed the northern flank of Company C; at 0905 the Company C line was probed again; and at 1250 Company A was tested. At 1340 Company B was probed, and at 1345 the Recondos'

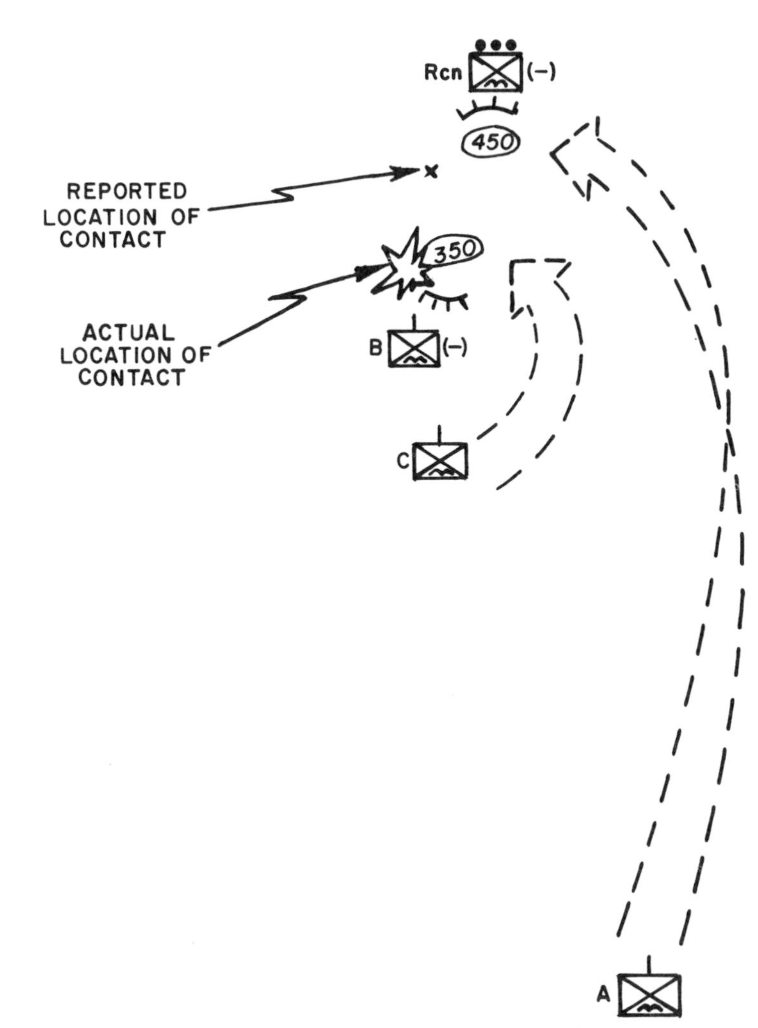

Diagram 4. Location of firefight.

position was reconnoitered. As a result of the enemy's reconnaissance, twelve North Vietnamese soldiers were killed. The North Vietnamese commander now knew that he was surrounded.

While the enemy reconnaissance was in progress, the Strike Force started to tighten its circle of forces. Using a loudspeaker in a helicopter, it tried to convince the 5th Battalion of the hopelessness of its situation. Two hours of broadcasting, however, brought no apparent results. By darkness of the 10th the entire Strike Force Battalion was deployed in a circle roughly 600 meters in diameter around Hill 450. A prisoner captured by Company C had reported that the remainder of the 5th North Vietnamese Army Battalion was on the hill.

In contrast to the C-47 illumination on the night of 9-10 November, Colonel Dietrich decided that continuous illumination was not required the night of 10-11 November. There were no gaps now in his circle of forces, and the enemy would be more easily destroyed if he moved out of his prepared positions. The enemy tested the ring five times that night: twice in the Company B area in the south, twice in the Company A positions in the east, and finally at 0340 the Recondos in the west. In each case the effort failed.

On the morning of the 11th, the 5th Battalion was greeted by renewed psychological operations. This broadcast came from a speaker on the ground with Companies B and C, which had started moving north up Hill 450. This time the enemy responded. One North Vietnamese soldier surrendered to Company C and appealed to his comrades to follow him. One more soldier surrendered to Company B. Then Company C captured seven enemy soldiers, and Company B captured two. Company A captured five soldiers, and the battalion staff with Company A captured two more. Companies B and C stopped at the top of Hill 450, and Company A swept the northern slope from east to west. They engaged a North Vietnamese machine gun and killed the crew.

The battle was over. The total number of bodies counted and enemy captured was seventy-five. Blood trails, parts of bodies, and prisoners indicated that many more had died. Of the thirty-six enemy soldiers captured, thirty-two were North Vietnamese Army troops. Fourteen crew-served weapons, including three of the battalion's four mortars; forty-four individual weapons; and substantial amounts of equipment, ammunition, and other supplies were also captured. U.S. casualties during the three-day period were five killed and fifteen wounded.

The battle of Phong Cao dramatically illustrates the use of the helicopter for command and control. It also demonstrates the application of established principles to new situations. The helicopter was described earlier as the most significant innovation of the war. Its value in command and control was confirmed many times in Vietnam. In the battle of Phong Cao, the helicopter permitted Colonel Dietrich to reach the point of contact in time to influence the battle. It also enabled him to locate the disoriented platoons on the ground, which indicated their positions with smoke and panels, and to insure their integration into his scheme of maneuver and fire support plan.

The unique enemy tactics in Vietnam offered the commanders of battalions and other small units opportunities for deception that had not existed in the Korean War or World War II. The tactics of the Strike Force Battalion during the battle of Phong Cao deceived the enemy into thinking that he was opposed by a small U.S. unit. "Even on 9 November when Company A conducted a heliborne assault . . . a

POW later captured stated that the NVA forces on Phong Cao Mountain thought they had the US forces surrounded until they attempted to break the contact and found it hopeless." Brigadier General Willard Pearson, who was the commanding general of the 1st Brigade, 101st Division, at the time of the battle of Phong Cao, described the concept as semiguerrilla tactics. These tactics emphasized stealth and deception through night operations, long-range patrols, reduction of helicopter traffic and other indications of U.S. operations, and similar techniques designed to foster contact with the enemy. Once contact was made, the units converted to conventional methods, using all available firepower, mobility, and reserves.

One of the most important aspects of semiguerrilla warfare was the ambush. The ambush had been used by the U.S. Army as far back as April 1775, when Colonel Smith's redcoat column was continuously ambushed as it withdrew from Concord, Massachusetts. The mechanical ambush, as it was used in Vietnam, however, was new. This innovation combined the ambush technique with the claymore mine and a trip wire. Later it was refined by the addition of a remote control firing device. In effect, this technique was an antipersonnel minefield with a fire–no fire option. Using the command-detonated mechanical ambush in conjunction with sensors increased its effectiveness. It was particularly appropriate in areas where firing devices that had to be triggered by the enemy were unsuitable because of civilian traffic.

The long-range patrol (LRP) was a particularly significant aspect of U.S. operations in Vietnam. Such patrols were not new to the U.S. Army, but they were used in increasing density and were now operating at division level. Long-range patrols were needed in Vietnam because of the difficult terrain assigned to the divisions and the elusiveness of the enemy. The helicopter and effective communications enabled the patrols to be more densely dispersed.

U.S. divisions formed provisional LRP units in 1965 and 1966, based on the success of the 5th Special Forces Group's Project Delta. The use of long-range patrols at division level prompted the development of a succession of minor innovations to support operations. Two of these developments were the LRP ration, a freeze-dried meal about one-third the weight of a C ration, and the McGuire rig, a device similar to a parachute harness, which was attached to a line suspended from a helicopter. The system was used to extract small patrols in situations where the helicopter could not land. A drawback of the McGuire rig was that the passenger rode to his destination suspended below the helicopter. This disadvantage was overcome in the jungle penetrator system, which was commonly used for field medical evacuation in Vietnam. The penetrator was lowered through the jungle canopy using a helicopter hoist, and the passenger, seated or standing on the penetrator, was lifted into the helicopter. For the seriously wounded, a basket litter was substituted for the jungle penetrator. In addition to these innovations, new tactics for depositing and picking up long-range patrols by helicopter were also developed.

The experiences of Company F (a long-range patrol), 51st Infantry, between Bien Hoa and Xuan Loc, fifty kilometers northeast of Saigon, are indicative of the effectiveness of long-range patrols. In Operation UNIONTOWN III–BOXSPRINGS, in February and March 1968, Company F was under the operational control of the 199th Infantry Brigade (Light) (Separate). The plan was for both light reconnaissance teams and heavy combat-reconnaissance teams to monitor trails and suspected river crossing sites in support of brigade operations. Taking prisoners of war was an additional mission of combat-reconnaissance teams. When the enemy's position could be fixed, reaction forces were committed to exploit the situation.

During the operation, patrols were sent out to fight the enemy 117 times with no U.S. losses, although there were forty emergency extractions. Viet Cong and North Vietnamese Army troops were sighted 91 times; contact was made 33 times, and a reaction force was committed on 10 occasions to exploit sightings or help extract the long-range patrols. Enemy troops killed in action numbered forty-eight, with twenty-six more probable. Eighteen prisoners of war or detainees were taken.

The tremendous intelligence advantage gained by the 199th Brigade through the use of long-range patrols is not evident in these figures. This advantage, however, is illustrated by the following comments made by Major General William R. Peers, when he commanded the 4th Infantry Division:

> In 1967, before we had any form of surveillance unit such as the people sniffer and the air cav with the scout unit, every major battle that the 4th Infantry Division got itself into was initiated by the action of a Long-Range Patrol; every single one of them. That included the battle of Dak To for the Long-Range Patrols completely uncovered the enemy movement. We knew exactly where he was coming from through our Long-Range Patrol action.

In support of the LRP effort, General William C. Westmoreland authorized the establishment of the MACV Recondo School in September 1966. The term "Recondo" is a combination of reconnaissance and commando and had been used to describe a ranger-type school organized in 1959 by General Westmoreland, when he commanded the 101st Airborne Division at Fort Campbell, Kentucky. This identification of Recondo with the men of the long-range patrols, who were generally considered to have the most uncomfortable and dangerous job in Vietnam, led to the use of the name by other units. The Recondo Platoon of the 2d Battalion (Airborne), 502d Infantry, was one such unit. The platoon could act as a long-

SOLDIERS TRAINING ON TROOP LADDERS SUSPENDED FROM CH-47. *The troop ladder was superior to the rappel rope because it could be used for recovery as well as insertion.*

range patrol since some of its members had been Recondo-trained, but the platoon was used as a maneuver unit in normal battalion operations. This innovation, the informal organization of a fourth maneuver element in the infantry battalions in Vietnam, was subsequently recognized in the authorization for a fourth rifle company.

Another technique of the 2d Battalion (Airborne), 502d Infantry, that was new in some respects was the stay-behind patrol. Stay-behind patrols were used during World Wars I and II and also during the Korean War. These forces, however, were generally small in order to facilitate their withdrawal through enemy lines and to aid in concealment. The fluidity of the battlefield in Vietnam and the availability of helicopters to reinforce or extract the stay-behind force led to frequent use of stay-behind patrols of various sizes among U.S. forces.

The following extract from the report of the 2d Battalion (Airborne), 502d Infantry, gives the achievements of the Strike Force's stay-behind patrol at Phong Cao.

> Three days after the conclusion of the battle, Company A, after an overt resupply, moved clandestinely back into the area and stayed approximately 4 days. During this period they uncovered one large medical cache and intercepted some enemy forces returning to the area. Some 2 days after Company A overtly moved out of the area, Company B clandestinely moved back into the Phong Cao mountain area as a followup force and uncovered another large medical and kitchen cache plus finding one wounded NVA soldier who had been hiding since about 12 November.

The use of deception was the key to the victory at Phong Cao mountain. The effective and easily understood deception plan was an excellent example of the adaptation of conventional tactics to an unconventional situation. The checkerboard search innovation, the long-range patrol, and the stay-behind force all contributed significantly to the success of the operations of the 2d Battalion (Airborne), 502d Infantry, at Phong Cao.

The way in which the long-range patrols were used was one of the most significant innovations of the war, and the use of the helicopter for command and control became a normal method of operation for virtually all tactical commanders in Vietnam. These innovations, except for the use of the helicopter, were adaptations of time-tested techniques and, in this sense, were characteristic of a large share of the innovations of the war. Confronted by an enemy who took advantage of any operational pattern that developed, the U.S. soldier in Vietnam soon learned that change was the order of the day and that innovation was the key to success.

CHAPTER XI

Suoi Cat (2 December 1966)

The battle of Suoi Cat provides an excellent example of the successful use of armor against the ambush tactics of the Viet Cong. The enemy in Vietnam was not invincible, and a trained outfit frequently took advantage of the mistakes and limitations of the Viet Cong or North Vietnamese Army. This practice applied to the mine threat as well, where the most successful tactic was to attack the man who placed the mine. The 11th Armored Cavalry—the "Blackhorse Regiment"—in the forefront of much of the action in the III Corps Tactical Zone, proved again the soundness of battle-tested doctrine and maneuver techniques for tanks and armored cavalry assault vehicles.

The enemy force in this battle was drawn from the 275th Viet Cong Regiment. This regiment was assigned the task of staging an ambush along National Highway 1 in Long Khanh Province just east of Suoi Cat. Order-of-battle experts had put the 275th Viet Cong Regiment well to the northwest, but the unit apparently made its way into the province sometime between late October and late November 1966. Four or five days before the 2 December battle, the 11th Armored Cavalry's intelligence officer received information based on agent reports of "movements north and south of Highway 1" near Suoi Cat and Chua Chan Mountain. This part of Highway 1, a traditional site for ambushes, inevitably came to be known as Ambush Alley. The ambush force, which was later estimated to be a reinforced battalion of the 275th Viet Cong Regiment, spent the latter part of November reconnoitering the ambush site and preparing positions complete with overhead protection. In typical Viet Cong fashion, maximum use was made of local cover, and withdrawal routes were plotted, principally to the south.

On 1 December 1966, Troop B, 1st Squadron, 11th Armored Cavalry, minus its 3d Platoon but reinforced by a platoon of tanks from the squadron's tank company, took over the security of the rock quarry at Gia Ray. In December, the Troop B commander sent a convoy to the regimental base camp near Xuan Loc to obtain supplies. The two tanks, three armored cavalry assault vehicles, and two

2½-ton trucks reached the base camp without incident. The supplies were loaded, and the group headed for Gia Ray at 1600 hours. The tank platoon leader, 1st Lieutenant Wilbert Radosevich, was the convoy commander and arranged his vehicles in the following order: tank, two armored cavalry assault vehicles (ACAV's), two supply trucks, ACAV, tank. A helicopter gunship on the convoy's radio frequency and a forward air controller were covering overhead. At Suoi Cat the convoy commander switched back from the squadron's radio net to the B Troop net as he cleared Chua Chan Mountain, which often distorted communications between Gia Ray and the regimental base. Since the 1st Squadron maintained a relay station on top of Chua Chan, the convoy commander's communications setup was excellent.

As the convoy moved east out of Suoi Cat, Lieutenant Radosevich noticed an ominous lack of activity along the road: no men or women, no children, no dogs. About two kilometers from the hamlet, the lieutenant turned in the commander's hatch and accidentally tripped the turret override, causing the main gun to swing to the right. Apparently seeing this movement, an enemy soldier prematurely detonated a mine about ten meters ahead of Lieutenant Radosevich's tank. The fight was on. The convoy commander, wounded by mine fragments, directed the odd numbered vehicles to fire to the left of the road and the even numbered vehicles to fire to the right, thereby establishing the herringbone formation. He also sent word to B Troop that the convoy was under attack; relief from several directions was on the way. Though hit repeatedly with recoilless rifle and rocket rounds, the combat vehicles kept moving through the kill zone and escorted the two trucks to safety in the direction of Gia Ray.

The Troop B commander, Captain John R. Landry, led a relief column of two tanks and three armored cavalry assault vehicles south out of Gia Ray toward the ambush. They were joined at the junction of Highways 1 and 333 by ACAV's from Captain Landry's 2d Platoon and plunged into the fray. The 2d Platoon suffered some fourteen nonfatal casualties from Viet Cong grenades as it neared the ambush site, but it herringboned its way into the battle with deadly effect. Elements of Company D took off from the regimental base seven minutes after the first report of contact, followed closely by Troop C and the howitzer battery. Ten minutes later, Troop A was on the way. Meanwhile, the helicopter gunship was making firing runs, and requests for artillery fire and air strikes had been sent. The tanks of Company D and the ACAV's of Troop C, in turn, raked the ambush site. Troop C moved east down Highway 1 to cover possible Viet Cong withdrawal routes. Troop A arrived just as some of the Viet Cong were attempting to leave their positions. Fifteen of the enemy were cut down before they could get away. The battle which began about 1640

M48 Tanks Halted in Herringbone Formation

hours was over by 1750, but sporadic fire from the Viet Cong continued until 1950. In an attempt to seal off escape routes, artillery and AC-47 "Spook" ships were used throughout the night. The Viet Cong lost at least ninety-nine men and suffered a stunning defeat. One U.S. soldier, a sergeant in the 27th Engineer Battalion, lost his life in the battle, and there were twenty-two other casualties in the Blackhorse Regiment.

The Viet Cong commander had selected the small resupply convoy as a target, perhaps believing that it could be easily overwhelmed. Normally quite skillful in the planning and execution of ambushes, the enemy at Suoi Cat committed a number of costly errors. The premature detonation of the mine was the first mistake. Although the killing zone was covered by light and heavy machine guns, 60-mm. mortars, small arms, at least one recoilless rifle, and an undetermined number of rocket-propelled grenade launchers, the Viet Cong were unable to achieve fire superiority in the first critical moments of the action. Having failed to stop either the lead or the rear tank, they were furthermore unable to cope with the ACAV's. The most disastrous mistake made by the enemy leader was to spring the ambush when U.S. relief units were so close. Within four minutes the tank platoon had reached the killing zone, and Troop B's 2d Platoon arrived in seven minutes. If the Viet Cong commander had been familiar with the potential of the ACAV in combat, very likely he would not have positioned his men so close to the road. Whatever the exact reasoning behind the location of the ambush force, it was exposed to the considerable and effective fire of ACAV machine gunners and grenadiers.

The Viet Cong positions, although out of range of the eight-inch howitzers at Xuan Loc, were soon taken under fire by the fast moving artillerymen of the 1st Squadron's self-propelled 105-mm. howitzer battery. The ability of the artillery to move rapidly from one position to another and to set up within range apparently was not taken into account by the Viet Cong ambush planner. The squadron's howitzer battery was joined at Suoi Cat by Battery B, 2d Battalion, 35th Artillery, a 155-mm. self-propelled unit. Some 1,700 rounds were fired by these two batteries during the fight.

By the time the Company D and Troop C reinforcements arrived, the Viet Cong commander realized that he had failed in his mission and that he must withdraw. Enemy fire was intensified before the appearance of A Troop to allow the Viet Cong to disengage and move to withdrawal routes. The timing of this move was poor, however, as the Blackhorse troopers caught many of the Viet Cong in the act of withdrawing.

Enemy mines, such as the command-detonated device used at Suoi Cat, were a constant threat to our forces. Although the U.S. Army did employ claymore mines as a weapon, most of its efforts in this area were concentrated on defense. Enemy mines and booby traps caused approximately 70 percent of the vehicle losses and 20 percent of the casualties. The enemy employed "nuisance mining," that is, scattering mines throughout an area rather than in well-defined minefields, on a scale never before encountered by U.S. forces. Mines and booby traps were usually installed at night by trained personnel who had detailed knowledge of the terrain. Through ingenious techniques in mine warfare, the Viet Cong successfully substituted mines and booby traps for artillery. Instead of conventional minefields covered by fire, the enemy hindered or prevented the use of supply roads and inhibited off-the-road operations by planting explosive devices in indiscriminate patterns. While he benefited directly by causing combat casualties, vehicle losses, and delays in tactical operations, equally important was the psychological effect. Just the knowledge that a mine or booby trap could be placed anywhere slowed combat operations and forced allied troops to clear almost the entire Vietnam road net every day.

In response, an Army-wide concentrated effort in strategic and tactical planning, research and analysis, and materiel development was focused on countermeasures for mines and booby traps. The Mine Warfare Center of the Headquarters, United States Army, Vietnam (USARV), conducted an extensive study of the Viet Cong and North Vietnamese mining operations, techniques, and ordnance. Major Walter C. Bell, the chief of the center, published a report, "Mine Warfare in Vietnam," as a guide for units in the field. Although he found that Viet Cong and North Vietnamese techniques varied from place to place, Major Bell was able to make some generalizations. The enemy did not use the traditional minefields of previous wars. He laid protective fields around the more permanent base camps but with no pattern, and the mines were certain to be booby-trapped. Major Bell also discovered that the enemy tended to mine the same sectors of roads repeatedly.

Major Bell divided the mining problem into three major categories: road mining, off-road antivehicular mining, and antipersonnel mining. Most U.S. mine casualties occurred during road clearing operations. Heavy losses coupled with the need to clear many kilometers of road every day put a strain on the engineer and combat troop effort. Off-road mines caused more damage to armored vehicles than road mining did. Little used trails and tracks, open fields, jungles, and even avenues that were difficult for vehicles to use were mined. The antipersonnel mines or booby traps were ingeniously rigged devices, set in unusual locations to trap the individual soldier. Such devices, normally made from materials at hand, were used on a massive scale. Virtually every enemy position was encircled or infested with them. From an extensive analysis of the techniques used by the enemy in each of the four corps tactical zones, the Mine Warfare Center marked on a map the areas where mining activity was heavy and qualified each area by indicating the most common type of mine there. Armed with this knowledge, the tactical commanders and individual soldiers were able to reduce U.S. casualties.

In the III Corps Tactical Zone, the Viet Cong seemed to adjust their mining pattern according to U.S. tactical operations, rather than following a preconceived plan. During periods when U.S. and allied activity was high, there was a substantial increase in the Viet Cong mining efforts. Roads and off-road tracked vehicle paths were the main targets. The problem facing the 11th Armored Cavalry in this area became one of inhibiting the enemy's road-mining activities. The regiment also learned that the mining and the setting of booby traps was largely the work of Viet Cong local forces rather than larger Viet Cong and North Vietnamese Army units.

The Army took extensive steps to educate all subordinate commands concerning mines and booby traps. Information which defined the mine threat in various areas was passed down through channels. Units prepared monthly reports that outlined mine warfare incidents, the types of mines or booby traps encountered, and their locations. The Mine Warfare Center distributed notes to all major USARV units to inform them of various techniques that might be useful in countering the explosive devices.

A further effort to educate troops was made by the Combined Intelligence Center, Vietnam. "Viet Cong/North Vietnamese Army Employment of Mines and Booby Traps" described all of the mines and booby traps used by the enemy in Vietnam. Included were foreign mines and fuzing devices, plus expedient mines and ingenious fuzing devices and trip wires used to detonate booby traps. All combat units used the documents and the experiences of division personnel to conduct mine warfare training for new arrivals.

U.S. forces unwittingly furnished many of the items from which the enemy fashioned mines and booby traps. Explosive material came from dud rounds and other ordnance lost or discarded by U.S. troop units. Empty C-ration cans and used batteries were prime components of Viet Cong mines. Field commanders conducted a constant antilitter campaign. Control of ammunition and policing of defensive positions were stressed.

Using the Rome plow in land clearing operations helped to reduce command-detonated mine incidents. Removing all vegetation from the sides of roads and around base camps eliminated enemy cover. The paving of roads proved to be one of the most effective means to counter enemy mines, since holes in the asphalt were difficult to dig and easy to identify. A good example was heavily mined Route 1 in Quang Ngai Province. Although culverts were still destroyed by the enemy, there were no mining incidents after the road was paved. A similar technique for unpaved roads was the daily use of oil or peneprime over an area previously cleared of mines. Enemy attempts to mine the road were then readily apparent. Another effective countermeasure used by many units in Vietnam was to encourage local citizens to report the location of mines in return for a cash reward. In

ENGINEER MINE CLEARING TEAM

1968, through this volunteer informant program, 103,521 pieces of ordnance that could have been used as mines and booby traps were located. Trained dogs were also effective in detecting these devices. In one test involving 131 road clearing missions, 157 area searches, and 2 village searches, the dogs found 19 mines and 33 booby traps.

Kits were developed for armored personnel carriers to provide supplemental armor for the hull bottom and to relocate and strengthen the fuel line. One armored personnel carrier on which the new armor kit was installed hit a twenty-pound mine with no casualties among the men on board.

Generally, mine detectors designed to locate metallic mines or minute pieces of metal were not effective. One method which combated the difficulty of detecting tiny metal detonators in dirt roads sprinkled with artillery fragments was to use the same minesweep team every day. The men became so familiar with the road that they were able to spot minor changes in the surface or the surrounding area. The majority of mines found were detected visually and destroyed with explosives in place.

Still being developed are various hand-held infrared detectors and others for use in helicopters and vehicles. Experiments were conducted to induce current in mine detonator wiring using radio frequencies. However, these experiments were unsuccessful and were terminated. A need for better protection of troops against the enemy's mine threat prompted the Combat Developments Command to consider mine protection in future vehicle developments. In addition, the U.S. Army Materiel Command continued its efforts to develop energy absorbing systems to reduce the shock of mine explosions.

The ENSURE 202 Tank-Mounted Expendable Mine Roller was tried in Vietnam as a mine-detonating device. Designed to exert high ground pressure without crushing roads and bridges, it was attached to a medium tank. Like the many rollers used in Vietnam and earlier, the problem was to survive the mine it detonated.

Tactical operations, including ambushing and patrolling, were designed to hit at the enemy's mining efforts. Countermine activities were oriented toward finding mines after they had been positioned and toward improving the ability of personnel and vehicles to survive an explosion. In Vietnam the U.S. forces attacked the source of the problem. The most useful technique was frequent ambush patrols in areas repeatedly mined. At times observation towers were constructed on routes in the vicinity. A reconnaissance in force was often conducted by cavalry units ten or fifteen minutes after a mine sweep to surprise the enemy who would lay mines behind the team. One unit in the III Corps Tactical Zone made a detailed study of enemy road-mining patterns. The analysis showed that 50 percent of such activity in the area of operations was concentrated in four sectors of road having a total length of about 4½ kilometers. Once the problem areas were isolated, sensor fields were installed and ambush patrol activity was increased. Artillery concentrations were plotted, night aircraft equipped with infrared lights were put on alert, and night observation devices were positioned so that the unit could respond to sensor activations and patrol sightings. After only one month the results were conclusive. The four road sectors, which had previously experienced fifty-six mining incidents per month, had only fifteen incidents during the test month. One sector went from fifteen to one.

In addition to tactics against enemy mining, countermeasures for ambushes were also developed. The objective of the herringbone technique, used so successfully at the battle of Suoi Cat, was to concentrate a formation of combat vehicles "sufficiently to achieve overwhelming firepower to the flanks while maintaining sufficient dispersion to force the enemy to employ aimed fire." An armored column could also herringbone its way down a line of march by applying the leapfrog technique. The first platoon halted in the herringbone pattern. The second platoon passed through the first and assumed the herringbone pattern. The third continued on through, and the process was repeated until a suspicious or particularly dangerous area

ENSURE 202 Roller on M48 Tank

had been crossed. If contact was made, the herringbone permitted the commander to "fix and hold an entire ambushing force," as in the case of Suoi Cat.

Naturally, the mere execution of the herringbone formation did not guarantee success in a counterambush effort. The shock of the initial enemy volley had to be countered with a withering blast of return fire even more shocking to the enemy soldiers. The 11th Armored Cavalry's counterambush training emphasized that gunners on odd numbered vehicles were to fire to the left; those on even numbered vehicles were to fire to the right. If there were no visible targets to engage, the .50-caliber gunners on the armored cavalry assault vehicles were to begin raking fire at fifty meters and the M60 gunners at twenty-five meters, and the men acting as grenadiers were to start heaving grenades over the sides of the vehicles. The ACAV's carried enough ammunition for about ten minutes of almost continuous firing. The inseparable factors of command and control played an especially vital role in counterambush tactics. The herringbone formation enabled a commander to move around his command, provide his men with more ammunition, and remove any wounded from the ambush zone. The herringbone pattern was useful as a base of fire while other elements maneuvered against the enemy and allowed the unit to communicate with the "outside world" and let those who could help him know that he had a problem. In the case of Suoi Cat, the lieutenant could contact his squadron, B Troop, the gunship, and the forward air controller. Either the gunship or the forward air controller could have acted as an airborne relay if necessary and could have provided invaluable route reconnaissance ahead of the convoy. Finally, the training of the entire squadron as a team and its dedication to the offense provided the extra drive and co-ordination needed to get the relief column on the way. Lieutenant Radosevich's small group gave a fine account of themselves; however, the timely arrival of other elements of the squadron carried the day.

The success of U.S. armor formations in Vietnam was the result of many factors. The herringbone and the maneuver aspects of the counterambush drill were the most obvious. Support by artillery, tactical air fighters, and helicopter gunships was less obvious but equally effective. Combined, these elements often neutralized the effectiveness of the enemy ambush.

The mining problem in Vietnam was never solved to the extent that operations could be conducted without provisions for mine detection. It was, however, reduced considerably by a combination of old and new techniques. The mine dog and new mine detectors were adaptations of earlier techniques, while the most significant innovation was the concept of engaging the minelayer before the mine was planted. This concept, to strike the problem at its source, was one of the most fundamental aspects of the war.

CHAPTER XII

Lam Son II (2-5 June 1966)

Operation Lam Son II provides a glimpse of some innovations which had nearly as great an impact on the struggle in Vietnam as the defeat of the enemy by force of arms. While the enemy must be destroyed or forced to surrender by a combination of firepower and maneuver, it is pacification which must end the unrest created by the enemy, improve the lot of the people, and build a cohesive, viable state. The weapons in this war may be the healing hands of a surgeon, a bag of rice, a loudspeaker message, or even toys for children. The 1st Infantry Division used weapons of this unconventional nature and incorporated psychological warfare in combat operations.

At 1530 on 2 June 1966, the first day of a successful hamlet festival in Tan Phuoc Khanh wound down with all the festivities of a county fair. The steady sound of the 1st Infantry Division Band had seemed out of place as it marched through the streets of the small Vietnamese village. It was not just a concert but a weapon in "the other war."

The seal and search of the village had started the evening before. While the rest of the division was preparing night patrols, selecting outpost locations, and digging in to establish night defensive positions, Major Henry J. Wereszynski's 1st Battalion, 26th Infantry, was conducting an airmobile assault to set up a cordon around Tan Phuoc Khanh and its 9,000 inhabitants. A combined force of five companies had been formed to cordon the village. Major Wereszynski had Companies A, B, and C with Troop A, 1st Squadron, 4th Cavalry, attached and the 7th Company, 7th ARVN Regiment, in support.

Lam Son II—a combined operation conducted by Headquarters, 1st Infantry Division Artillery, and Headquarters, 5th ARVN Division—had started with a highly successful hamlet search and "county fair" operation on 26 May 1966 in Binh Chuan village. Because of the wide publicity, the cordon and seal of Tan Phuoc Khanh had to be completed as quickly as possible to offset the loss of surprise. The helicopter would be a valuable tool in providing the necessary speed.

The mission was to pacify the village, conduct a thorough search, root out the Viet Cong infrastructure, gather intelligence, and "win

1st Infantry Division Band Performing at Tan Phuoc Khanh

the hearts and minds of the people." Planning and execution involved close teamwork between U.S. and Vietnamese forces. There was no single commander in charge, but rather a combined staff of both Vietnamese and U.S. personnel from the two headquarters was formed.

As the airmobile force was flying toward its landing zones, Major Wereszynski, in the command and control ship, was reviewing the plan in his mind. Company A would assault into a zone north of the village, Company B would be on the east, and Company C would land in the south. Troop A, 1st Squadron, 4th Cavalry, and 7th Company, 7th ARVN Regiment, were already moving overland to complete the cordon. As the air assault ended, the ground elements were moving into position. The village was sealed at 2010 hours on 1 June 1966. Later that night Company A was moved by air mobile assault farther north to cut off possible Viet Cong escape routes.

At 0605 hours 2d Company, 7th ARVN Regiment, moved into the village. Loudspeakers proved to be extremely valuable in reducing the alarm of the villagers, advising them what to do, and providing a means of control. While the external cordon remained in position, 2d Company soldiers established additional cordon lines to further divide the hamlet into three sections. Search forces from Binh

WOMAN WINS YORKSHIRE PIG IN LOTTERY *at another hamlet festival.*

Duong Province soon followed and spread throughout the village to begin the search. The force had been tailored to fit the needs of this operation and contained many different types of U.S. and Vietnamese units.

The first step was to assemble all men between the ages of fifteen and forty-five. These men were moved to the National Police headquarters in Phu Cuong for additional screening. Next came the real heart of the cordon and search operation: the hamlet festival. The festival was designed to display the concern of the Vietnamese government for the welfare of the people. The start was sounded by the Binh Duong Province band at 0830 hours. By 0900 hamlet residents began arriving in the central area and were greeted by personnel from province headquarters.

Although not used at Tan Phuoc Khanh, several tactical units conducted a lottery during county fair operations. Instructions or information to villagers were distributed by means of leaflets, which were stamped with lottery numbers. These leaflets helped control the people and, at the same time, maintain their interest in the program. The winners received household items as prizes.

The hamlet festival can best be compared to a small town's fall carnival with speeches by candidates who are running for office. To

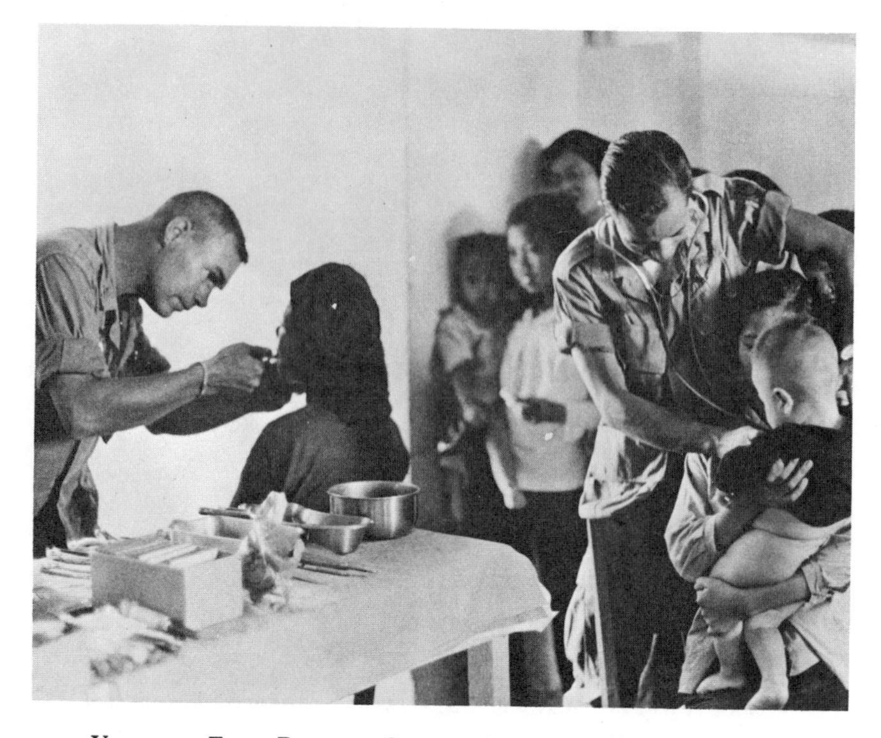

VILLAGERS FROM REFUGEE CAMP IN BIEN HOA PROVINCE RECEIVE TREATMENT DURING A MEDCAP

the children it was all fun and games. Likewise, the adults found it enjoyable and were interested to hear about national programs from a government official. In a war of insurgency, such an operation is the essence of the fight.

As the people gathered in the entertainment area, the 5th ARVN Division band began the Vietnamese national anthem. Coupled with the bright red and yellow Vietnamese banners and flags, this action conveyed to the people the presence of a government—one that cared. It was a welcome feeling in the midst of a protracted war. The national anthem was followed by a performance of traditional dances and pantomimes by the 5th ARVN Division cultural teams. Then the province chief, Lieutenant Colonel Ba, and the district chief, Captain Phuc, explained the government program to the people and urged them to support the government cause. Colonel Ba stayed all day talking to elders and heads of households.

The hamlet festival was a collection of several functions. The Medical Civic Action Program (MEDCAP) station was manned by medical personnel from one of the U.S. units. The staff normally included a doctor, medical specialists, Vietnamese interpreters, and sometimes a dentist. The operation was conducted like a "sick call" and held in conjunction with psychological activities. The medical treatment was mainly symptomatic—aspirin for pains, soap and medication for skin diseases, and extraction for toothaches. Serious medical cases were referred to other facilities outside the military channels for proper treatment or corrective surgery. The Youth Service Activity entertained the children so that the parents were free. Games were played, songs were sung, candy and toys were handed out to the children, and movies were shown. At one point Colonel Ba joined the children for a game of ball. The Vietnamese Agricultural Service provided information to the elders about farming and explained to the villagers how the government was prepared to assist the farmer. This service was very popular with the people.

At 1200 an American luncheon of hot dogs, potato salad, milk, juice, and all the extras was served. Although the people commented about the strange taste of the food, they all returned for second and third helpings. The meal was an interesting change from their normal rice-heavy diet.

The psychological operations and civil affairs teams performed several duties. They helped direct and control the people at first and mingled with the crowd, talking to small groups. They were able to discuss government opportunities and learn what the citizens needed and wanted from the government. The real purpose of the hamlet festival was to bring the government to the people and, at the same time, to turn an intelligence operation into an activity that the citizens would find pleasant. A major objective was to eliminate the Viet Cong infrastructure. All civilians were therefore required to pass through identification stations for an interview, a check of their identification cards, and the issue of special passes. This process allowed the detection of false identification papers and the selection of persons for further screening. Other stations were established for persons who wanted to volunteer information. Rice was given to all persons during the interviews.

By the time the 1st Infantry Division Band paraded through the streets, the results were becoming evident. Of the 740 men who had been sent to Phu Cuong for screening earlier in the day, 29 were found to be Viet Cong suspects, 9 were army deserters, 4 possessed false identification cards, 13 were former Viet Cong who had violated the limits of their probation, and 62 were South Vietnamese draft dodgers. The search of the village had turned up 25 additional Viet Cong suspects, including 3 women carrying medical supplies and 10 men hiding in haystacks and wooded areas. The scout dogs had discovered two tunnels in the village.

During the day 325 individuals had been interrogated at the identification stations. Two of these were identified as Viet Cong, one allegedly the Viet Cong village secretary. A sketch of the U.S. Phu Loi Base Camp was found on the body of a Viet Cong killed during the assault to establish the cordon.

The cordon force remained in position throughout the night, and on 3 June the festival continued. Selected areas were again searched. The western portion of the village yielded forty-eight more Viet Cong suspects. They were hiding in haystacks, tunnels, woodpiles, and watchtowers. By the end of the second day, the festival had succeeded in softening and changing the attitudes of many individuals who had been hostile to the government. The operation was such a success that it was extended for a third day. By the end of the festivities, the civilian population truly wanted to assist friendly units in securing their village. One woman was given 200 piasters for volunteering information leading to the apprehension of a Viet Cong suspect hiding in a coffin. A confirmed Viet Cong led an intelligence platoon to a weapons cache that also contained Viet Cong tax collection statistics. He had decided to return to the government of Vietnam as a result of the hamlet festival. Many individuals spoke of Viet Cong harassment tactics in the village and stated that if they had sufficient security many more people would come there to live.

The cordon and search coupled with a hamlet festival was truly an innovation in civil affairs and psychological operations. "The primary accomplishment was the demonstration of an effective technique to bring government, including necessary force to initiate law and order, to a contested hamlet. Without the cordon and search the operation would have been merely a festival. Without the festival the operation would have been another 'police action.' Together, the effort [was] a useful means to begin a pacification drive."

At 0400 hours on 5 June 1966, the task force was moved a few hundred meters to the north to Hoa Nhut hamlet for the next operation. A pattern had been established to hit the Viet Cong at their most vital point—their infrastructure. Information acquired at a later date indicated that the Viet Cong had reviewed the Tan Phuoc Khanh operation and had estimated that they had lost 50 percent of their effectiveness. They also figured that two months would be needed to recoup their losses.

In a country like Vietnam, where citizens are subjected to the pressures and terrorism of an insurgent force and where the power and aims of the legitimate government are questioned and tested each day, any action or incident that shows the individual citizen that his government is interested and concerned in his welfare is highly effective. The hamlet festival served this purpose well.

In previous experience, guerrilla forces represented the government that had been displaced by the invading army. In Vietnam the guerrilla force represented an external power. Acts of terrorism were directed not at the invading army but rather at the innocent civilian. All actions were designed to discredit the existing government and to win the citizens over to the enemy. This situation changed the whole concept of civil affairs activities. In the words of Major General Melvin Zais, former commanding general of the 101st Airborne Division, "a well organized and managed effective civic action effort is absolutely essential to the attainment of our aims in Vietnam."

The civil affairs general staff officer (G-5) became increasingly important to the commander who was planning operations. In Major General Donn R. Pepke's 4th Infantry Division, "civil affairs teams [were] employed daily in support of tactical operations." While the operations general staff officer (G-3) was making plans for engaging and destroying the enemy force in an area, the G-5 was planning methods and operations to win the loyalty and support of the local civilian population. This aspect was a significant change from World War II, when civil affairs and civic action were conducted after the hostilities had ended.

A planning and control organization was obviously needed at brigade and battalion levels to deal with the problems involving civilians. A temporary arrangement was made at first, but the experience gained and the lessons learned early in the 1965 buildup prompted the creation of the civil-military operations field. This action led to the designation of an S-5, civil affairs officer, in every separate brigade.

The use of loudspeakers, the artillery of the civil affairs officer, became a fine art in Vietnam. The 1st Cavalry Division (Airmobile) supported ground operations with loudspeakers borne by helicopters. Divisions issued 1,000-watt loudspeaker equipment to each brigade and sometimes to battalions. As a result of this practice, if prisoners were taken or defectors encountered during tactical operations, the units were able to react quickly to the opportunity to use these men in developing loudspeaker appeals to their former comrades. In the 3d Brigade, 82d Airborne Division, such an appeal was then transmitted by the defector talking over a PRC-25 radio to a helicopter that rebroadcast the message while flying over his former unit. Thus the helicopter again demonstrated its importance in Vietnam by enhancing psychological operations. Major General Albert E. Milloy, 1st Infantry Division, stated: "Aerial PSYOP proved most effective when employed in the quick reaction role, in support of troops in contact, or for immediate exploitation of ralliers." Psychological operations were also carried on by frontline troops using bullhorns or hand-held megaphones. Messages from a newly captured prisoner or a defector were broadcast to enemy units still fighting. In September 1966 an enemy soldier rallied with his weapon to a 1st Infantry Division unit and was immediately interrogated by the G-5. A loud-

MEMBER OF 8TH PSYOP BATTALION AND HIS MONTAGNARD LOUDSPEAKER TEAM *broadcast propaganda message.*

speaker tape was produced in which the rallier talked about the good treatment he was receiving and asked former company members, by name, to surrender. Within twenty-four hours, eighty-eight members of the unit defected.

Leaflets were used separately or to complement loudspeakers. A multilith press was provided at the division level for quick reaction. On 13 May 1970 an agent reported that within Phong Dinh Province some 300 local force Viet Cong were to be recruited and sent to Cambodia as replacements for North Vietnamese Army units that had suffered heavy losses. The information was passed to the U.S. intelligence adviser and the province adviser for psychological operations. By 1600 on the same day, the psychological operations staff had prepared a leaflet capitalizing on the raw intelligence information. The priority target selected for the operation was the area of Phong Dinh Province, which was known to harbor hard-core Viet Cong. The province adviser for psychological operations and the S-5 adviser arranged to have the leaflets distributed throughout the appropriate districts during that night and the next day. Late in the evening on 14 May, the first *Hoi Chanh* rallied in Phung Hiep District with a copy of

DEPARTMENT OF THE ARMY
HEADQUARTERS 1ST INFANTRY DIVISION
OFFICE OF THE COMMANDING GENERAL

AVDB-CG 22 March 1967

SUBJECT: Unsoldierly Conduct of Officers of Cong Truong 9

TO: Commanding General
Cong Truong 9
HT 86500 YK

Dear General:

This is to advise you that during the battle at Ap Bau Bang on 20 March the Regimental Commander of Q763 and his Battalion Commanders disgraced themselves by performing in an unsoldierly manner.

During this battle with elements of this Division and attached units your officers failed to accomplish their mission and left the battlefield covered with dead and wounded from their units.

We have buried your dead and taken care of your wounded from this battle.

Sincerely,

J. H. HAY
Major General, USA
Commanding

One Side of Personalized Propaganda Leaflet. *Other side carried translation.*

the leaflet in his hand. By 23 May, twenty-eight Viet Cong had rallied, stating that they had done so because they were afraid of being sent to Cambodia. In a campaign to attract more ralliers through personal messages, the 101st Airborne Division gathered photographs of known Viet Cong operating in its area of operations. The families were asked to prepare personal messages to their relatives in the Viet Cong forces. Their messages, together with the appropriate photograph, were made into leaflets and dropped in the area where the individual was thought to be operating.

The S-5 of the 2d Brigade, 1st Infantry Division, developed a "white envelope" concept, designed to reach soldiers in the Viet Cong forces and the infrastructure with personalized messages from their families. Each family with relatives in the Viet Cong forces was given a white envelope containing a *Chieu Hoi* (open arms) appeal, rally instructions, a safe conduct pass, and a letter of amnesty from the local village or district chief. The intention was that the family would deliver the material to the Viet Cong member. This technique directed psychological pressure against both the family and the individual target.

The success of personal messages was best described by a Vietnamese who took advantage of this opportunity.

> My family lived under communist control for more than ten years, and I was forced to work for the Viet Cong. I was constantly afraid of being hit by American artillery, and I was seldom allowed to see my wife, even though I was a local guerrilla.
>
> Then I found a *Chieu Hoi* pass dropped by an American helicopter. My wife and some friends told me that it would be good to be a *Hoi Chanh* [a person who has rallied], but I hesitated for many weeks.
>
> One day I came back from an operation to find that my wife had taken our children to Lam Son, out of VC reach. So, with the pass sewed to the lining of my shirt, I waited for my chance to escape NVA control, and turned myself over to the GI's.
>
> Since then I have been trained to do scout work. I can see my wife and children every week, and am happy working with the 1st Division soldiers.

Several innovations were introduced to assist the interpreter at the lowest level frontline unit. Bilingual questionnaires were prepared which enabled commanders to gather intelligence and develop appeals quickly for psychological purposes. In March 1970 another infantry division initiated the idea of a bullhorn booklet to aid in the production of rapid-reaction messages. The booklet contained twenty-four printed messages, varying from appeals to warnings about restricted areas. The tactical units could select an appropriate message and have a Vietnamese broadcast it immediately. Other units used multilingual tapes. The 1st Infantry Division obtained excellent results from trilingual tapes, which were based on the ethnic background of civilians in an area.

The greatest innovation made in the G-5 area during the course of the Vietnam War was the increase in importance of psychological operations, civil affairs, civic action, and populace and resources control. Whereas before, G-5 activities had been viewed as supporting an operation after the fighting had ended, they were now integrated into the combat operation plan itself. Commanders and staff officers at battalion, brigade, and division levels learned that combat operations ultimately supported pacification, not vice versa.

CHAPTER XIII

Cu Chi

Vietnam was a different war. It was a conflict where the front line was not a trace on a map but was rather wherever the opposing combat forces met and fought. The secure rear areas of past wars that were so necessary for support were nonexistent in Vietnam. Only the areas that a commander actively secured could be used for support activities. This situation resulted in the base camp. The same security problem required convoy operations in a hostile environment, and better ways to conduct such operations had to be found. New techniques in automatic data processing were developed so that the machines could be used to support tactical activities. Finally, the widespread use of Army aircraft led to new and more efficient methods of maintaining the planes and helicopters.

The quiet of the 25th Infantry Division base camp at Cu Chi was shattered by explosions from incoming rocket rounds exactly one hour after midnight on 9 May 1968. Thirty rounds of 122-mm. and 107-mm. rockets, fired without warning from the surrounding area, rained down on the U.S. camp. The officer on duty at the 2d Brigade tactical operations center needed no confirmation from the bunker line as he switched on the base sirens and announced Condition RED. Forces on the perimeter were doubled, staffs of major units raced from their tactical operations centers, and troop units were readied to move to secondary defense positions. Word went out to a nearby fire support base, the local ARVN headquarters, and II Field Force headquarters that the base camp was under attack.

Two Cobra helicopters from Troop D, 3d Squadron, 4th Cavalry, in the air soon after the last rocket fell, radioed base camp defense and the artillery net. By this time the direction of the attack had been estimated, and previously positioned defense artillery had been fired. The two gunships searched the suspected enemy launch area and adjusted U.S. artillery accordingly.

As the battle quieted down, each sector of the bunker line called in to report all clear. An ARVN patrol in Vinh Cu, just south of the base, had had no contact. Nearby fire support bases, the Cu Chi subsector headquarters, and the units at Phu Cong and Ba Bep bridges reported that all was quiet. In two hours the camp commander decided that no ground attack was coming, and word went out to go to Condition YELLOW and finally, at 0300, to return to Condition WHITE.

The incident was another standoff attack.

Intelligence had forecast no high point of enemy activity, and there had been no indication of such. The rockets might even have been fired from unattended and locally fabricated launchers. According to a captured enemy rocket company commander:

> U.S. forces in Vietnam are disposed in large fixed installations which always provide our forces with lucrative targets. Our forces are always certain that as long as the weapons hit the installation, the U.S. forces will lose equipment and manpower. Likewise, these large posts do not have sufficient forces to control the surrounding countryside, which makes our attacks easier.

The G-3, operations general staff officer, ordered a reconnaissance in force in the suspected launch area the next morning; everybody not on duty at the perimeter or in the various support units and headquarters went back to sleep. By noon, two slightly wounded mechanics were back on duty, and a battered five-kilowatt generator was hauled to the salvage yard. (The above story is a composite account of an actual attack on Cu Chi and typical results and reactions by the division.)

These standoff attacks were designed to destroy allied military assets and weaken morale at minimum risk to the enemy. Moreover, they demonstrated the enemy's ability to attack and inflict damage on major U.S. and Republic of Vietnam installations at a time and place of his own choosing. The propaganda value was high, and at times the damage was significant. A considerable part of U.S. military resources was used to protect these fixed installations.

Cu Chi was surrounded by a large cleared area, including a man-made lake backed up by Ann Margaret Dam, which was built by Lieutenant Colonel Edward C. Gibson's 65th Engineer Battalion. The bunker line consisted of observation towers, firing positions with overhead cover, an earth berm, barbed wire entanglements, spotlights, and minefields. The support battalions camped at Cu Chi were assigned sectors of the defensive perimeter with very specific, rehearsed plans for reinforcement and counterattack. Artillery, countermortar fire, sensors, communications, reconnaissance, combat patrols, air support, and pacification all worked together to permit a large logistic and command complex to survive in no man's land.

In Vietnam, the base camp was a place where the individual soldier could train, take care of his equipment, and get some rest and relaxation. It also provided a full-time home for the larger tactical headquarters and the support units. The reason for developing such a facility was given by General William C. Westmoreland:

> Because of the nature of the war, tactical units had to be scattered throughout the nation at widespread locations. The lack of a sophisticated transportation system necessitated major units establishing their own logistic bases rather than one central depot serving a number of units. . . .

No activity could survive unless it was protected against ground attack and tied into the network of combat support. Supplies, maintenance facilities, hospitals and rest centers, airfields, administrative offices, and artillery were all located within bases to protect them against the enemy's assassination squads, local forces, standoff attacks, sappers, and main force units.

Being a semipermanent and vital installation, Cu Chi was selected with an eye to water supply, drainage, vegetation, and soil composition. Enough land was acquired to allow expansion of the camp and adequate fields of fire. Like many such camps, Cu Chi was situated close enough to a local civilian community to require constant attention to the perimeter's defense. Finally, supply routes around Cu Chi were such that a base camp could also be developed and supported administratively and logistically. As one brigade commander summed it up, "The guiding principle is to conduct the business of the base camp so that it supports the maximum of the brigade's needs and detracts the minimum from the brigade's tactical operations."

The 25th Division's planning in preparation for the construction of Cu Chi was unique. At their vantage point in Hawaii, division personnel received large-scale map coverage of the future division area from the United States Army Pacific Mapping and Intelligence Center. These maps enabled the planners to select and analyze a base camp site. After the division's advance party arrived in Vietnam and inspected the site, the base development plans were put into final form. The assistant division commander for support, Brigadier General Edward H. de Saussure, headed a base camp development committee that included in its membership the chief of staff, the G-4 (assistant chief of staff for logistics), the division engineer, the division signal officer, and representatives from the major units that would be occupying the camp. The clearing of fields of fire and the construction of bunkers and wire barriers had first priority. The various battalion cantonment areas were selected, and the road and telephone line networks were designed and approved. Before the division left Hawaii, it obtained precut tent and latrine kits. The kits were assembled by each unit in the division, packaged or banded, and shipped with unit cargo to Vietnam. At the site, these tent frames and latrines were easily erected in the designated unit areas and "added immeasurably in establishing the living areas prior to the arrival of the monsoon season." Within a relatively short time after the division arrived at the Cu Chi base, work began on semipermanent buildings.

To improve base camp living conditions without waiting for an overworked supply system to function, the division had left for Vietnam with ice machine plants, 65-cubic-foot walk-in refrigerators, 10-kilowatt generator sets, ice chests, and folding cots. Also taken along were filing cabinets, desks, chairs, tables, safes, tools, tentage, and communications equipment that came under the general heading of "post, camp, and station" property. Improvements in facilities and living conditions at Cu Chi progressed steadily. Maintenance shelters, fuel storage areas, ammunition bunkers, roads, and hardstands were built. Much of the construction was regulated by formal stateside procedures, and a great deal was done on a self-help basis because there were not enough engineers to go around. In the hot wet climate, SEA (Southeast Asia) huts were far cheaper and better than tents for semipermanent use. As these wooden huts were erected, Cu Chi took on the look of a real city.

Post engineer functions were performed under a contract administered by the Army headquarters at Long Binh. The contractor provided central power, certain building and ground maintenance, fire protection, and supervision of a variety of hired-labor jobs.

Although living conditions were austere, the fixed bases allowed a permanence undreamt of in World War II and Korea. The costs of operations to enhance morale were insignificant in comparison with their value. A large PX served the residents of the camp and frequently the fire bases and the troops in the field. Cu Chi had virtually all of the facilities found at permanent military installations outside Vietnam. The list included small clubs for officers, noncommissioned officers, and enlisted men; a USO club; barber shops; a MARS (Military Affiliate Radio System) station; a Red Cross field office and clubmobile unit; sports fields; miniature golf courses; swimming pools; and chapels. These troop support facilities, the occasional respites for the fighting units at division "Holiday Inns," the outstanding medical service, the one-year tour, and the rest and recuperation program contributed to the virtual elimination of incapacitating combat fatigue. More than 1,000 men a month left Cu Chi for five-day holidays in Hong Kong, Bangkok, Tokyo, Manila, Singapore, Penang, Taipei, Australia, or Hawaii. Additional rest and recuperation facilities were available at the beach resort in Vang Tau.

The base camp, at times, caused considerable consternation to the combat commanders. It tended to devour their combat resources and become "the tail that wagged the dog." At Cu Chi the 2d Brigade commander was usually appointed to run the camp, and he named a full-time deputy to supervise the administrative details of camp operation, base camp defense, and personnel overhead. All commanders found that "semipermanent base camps require manpower, equipment, and services beyond the organic capabilities of battalions, brigades, and divisions." By 1968 the Department of the Army had

SCENES AROUND CU CHI BASE CAMP

approved a personnel increase for base camps. This measure was a great help to the commander. The camp at Cu Chi and the two other base camps in the division at one time had an augmentation of ap-

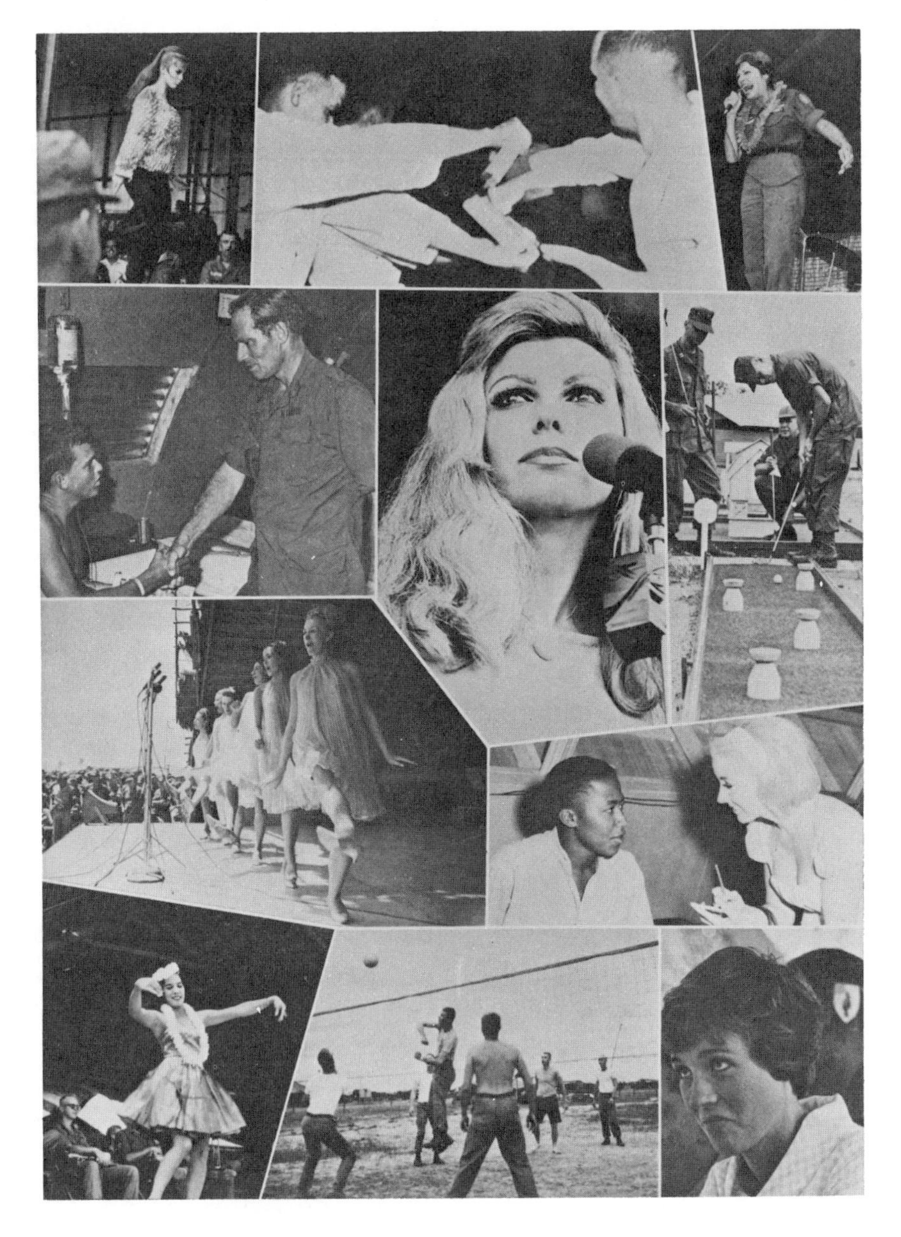

SPECIAL SERVICES ACTIVITIES AT CU CHI BASE CAMP

proximately 500 officers and enlisted men. This number was trimmed to around 100 by early 1969.

Generally, logistic support at base camps came from divisional and nondivisional units. As a rule the 25th Infantry Division Support

Command (DISCOM) provided supply and maintenance support for nearby tactical operations direct from Cu Chi and the two other division base camps, Tay Ninh and Dau Tieng. The support command sent along forward support elements for operations farther away and also supplied all of the various landing zones, fire support bases, and other tactical unit locations. Forward support activities and logistic support activities from the 1st Logistical Command provided additional support. A forward support activity was a provisional organization set up in the vicinity of the forward operating base of a tactical unit. As described in one report: "It is deployed to support a specific tactical operation when the tactical organic support capability is not sufficient to provide the support required." By contrast the logistic support activity was a "continuing activity, generally located in a fixed base camp to provide direct and general supply, maintenance, and service support to US and FWMAF (Free World Military Assistance Forces) on an area basis." By way of illustration, the 29th General Support Group of the Saigon Support Command was the major nondivisional unit charged with "across-the-board" logistic support in the 25th Infantry Division's tactical area of responsibility. The 29th General Support Group set up forward support areas for the 25th Division on such operations as MANHATTAN and YELLOWSTONE. Although the 29th did not establish a logistic support activity as such at Cu Chi, subordinate units of the group were based there and furnished direct and general support supply and maintenance and certain services to the division base camp. A logistic support activity was organized at the Tay Ninh base camp in support of the 1st Brigade and other tenant units.

The primary means of resupplying Cu Chi and the other base camps in the area of the 25th Infantry Division was by road. The 25th Supply and Transport Battalion and the 1st Logistical Command ran an average of four convoys, totaling 268 vehicles, a day on the highway between Cu Chi and the supply complex in the Long Binh-Saigon area. Division supply routes varied, from those strictly in enemy territory to those that were fairly safe for allied forces during daylight hours. In contested areas, major military operations were conducted to open roads to convoy traffic. Usually, effective convoy operations were possible only because of the mutually supporting artillery fire support bases along the route. Patrols, ambushes, and local search and destroy operations were conducted near the road. These techniques allowed convoys to travel with minimum escort. If the situation warranted, permanent outposts were provided to secure critical bridges and defiles. These outposts patrolled the road to prevent mining and ambushing.

In August 1968 the 25th Division developed new, aggressive convoy procedures to reduce losses. The convoys were divided into smaller, self-sufficient march units. Ammunition and fuel vehicles were placed at the rear to prevent an entire convoy from being blocked by burning vehicles, and wreckers and spare tractors were added to keep traffic moving. Military police elements provided control. A major innovation was having the convoy commander airborne over each convoy, from where he directed all march units and security forces. Armored vehicles were outposted at critical points along the route rather than moving with the convoy, as had been the practice. Gunship cover was arranged ahead of time over potential ambush sites. In areas where the road passed through jungles and plantations, Rome plows were used to clear potential ambush sites well back from both sides.

In the fall of 1968, a convoy operating under the revised procedures began to assemble. Unknown to the men, the enemy was preparing an ambush in a rubber plantation seventeen kilometers to the north. This attack was to be the first test of the new procedures. Before the convoy moved out, the area commanders flew over the most likely ambush sites. Combat elements were positioned at several possible sites, and the route was swept for mines and booby traps.

The last stretch of road over which the convoy was to pass was flanked by relatively flat terrain where a rubber plantation had recently been cleared of vegetation. The first and half of the second march units had entered the plantation when mortar rounds began falling all around them. Recoilless rifles, rocket-propelled grenades, and automatic weapons were fired at the convoy from both sides of the road. The training and orientation of convoy personnel quickly paid off. Vehicles short of the ambush halted and organized local security. Drivers moved damaged vehicles off the roadway, allowing other vehicles in the killing zone to continue to their destination.

The enemy force was immediately engaged by the convoy's security elements. Previously positioned reaction forces moved against the enemy's rear while preplanned artillery fire, gunships, and tactical air strikes took their toll. When the battle was over, the division counted seventy-three enemy dead and had captured large quantities of weapons and equipment. Allied losses were light. The enemy ambushers were soundly defeated.

In the following months the enemy attacked several more convoys. In every instance he failed to halt the fleeting target because he was overwhelmed by a massive U.S. reaction. The division had turned a defensive situation into a highly profitable offensive maneuver.

The use of convoy operations as a tool of pacification was a unique innovation. In the 25th Division the convoy was often used even when aerial resupply would have been easier. The reason for this maneuver was to open and expand the road network to strengthen friendly forces in the area. As soon as it became relatively safe for military convoys, civilian commercial vehicles could also use the route. This action had a direct and often phenomenal influence on the South Vietnamese people; they flowed back into the area, repaired their homes, and began to farm the countryside.

The electronic computer as an increasingly effective management tool was introduced into the combat headquarters in Vietnam. The Field Artillery Data Computer, already familiar to the artilleryman, the UNIVAC 1005, and the NCR (National Cash Register) 500 were used by the Tropic Lightning Division for routine artillery fire and survey programs and administrative management; and they were ultimately used to assist the commander in making decisions. Automatic data processors at Cu Chi became involved in providing information to many elements within the division as well as to command elements in Vietnam, Hawaii, and the United States. They used standardized Army data systems that interfaced with command and support elements external to the division and with programs developed by their own personnel for the support of division elements.

The standard systems provided support in the areas of personnel, finance, and logistics. The standard Personnel Management and Accounting Card Processor (PERMACAP) system linked the division with ASMIS (A)—Major Army Subordinate Command Management Information System (Armywide personnel reporting system)—to provide information on the individual 25th Division soldier through channels to the Pentagon. It also produced recurring reports and rosters for personnel management within the division. The programs and procedures for the system were developed and maintained by the U.S. Army Computer System Command (USACSC). The UNIVAC 1005 computer equipment was mounted in mobile expansible vans parked outside the division's tactical operations center. The PERMACAP system provided timely and accurate data, reduced clerical effort, and eliminated duplication in the personnel support area.

Another standard Army system used at Cu Chi was the direct support unit-general support unit (DSU-GSU) system operated by the 725th Maintenance Battalion. This system provided stock control and inventory accounting for repair parts. The same programs and equipment are used by Army personnel at 150 installations in the United States and five foreign countries. The DSU-GSU system uses an NCR 500 computer and a variety of components from other manufacturers. On 29 October 1966 the 25th Division received its system, which soon began to provide timely, complete, and accurate spare parts handling as well as increased management reports to commanders. The system also fed data to higher headquarters and, in turn, to supply depots in the continental United States.

The standard system used to pay the soldiers of the 25th Division was called Military Pay, Vietnam. It was developed by the U.S. Army

Finance and Comptroller Information Systems Command and used the UNIVAC 1005 computer.

The 25th Division started early in the war to develop many uses for its automatic data processing equipment in support of operational planning. By 1970, Major General Harris W. Hollis had concluded:

> In no other war have we been so deluged by so many tidbits of information for we have been accustomed to an orderliness associated with established battle lines. Here, though, we have had to make our decisions based not upon enemy regimental courses of action, but rather upon the numerous isolated communist squad-sized elements. So with the scale down of the level of operations, we have had to increase our reliance on objective analysis of logical courses of action.

The computer reduced the time required to analyze and interpret information. The commanders obtained a better picture of the enemy and were able to exploit valuable information quickly. At Cu Chi all the input for computer analysis was taken from existing reports, and with the computer working on a 24-hour schedule, no significant interference with other activities occurred. A typical application was the use of the UNIVAC 1005 to analyze the threat from deadly mines and booby traps in the division area.

The maneuver unit operation summary program analyzed the date and times of combat operations, size and type of operations, type of support provided, and, most important, results obtained in each case. The program identified the most successful type of operation in each of the twenty-six subdivisions of the area of operations. A major by-product of the program was an indication of changes in enemy tactics soon after they occurred.

The enemy base camp denial program used dates and time, unit size and designation, type of terrain, co-ordinates, type of operation, fire support, and results of contacts. It indicated which types of operations were most successful in each enemy base camp area. It provided records of these operations and indicated which areas would most likely contain significant enemy forces. As a result, scheduling and planning of operations in enemy base camp areas improved.

The UNIVAC 1005 was also used as a file update and printing device, with little computing being done. Lists of known and suspected Viet Cong were updated and printed on a recurring basis to provide a ready source of current intelligence. This form of automation permitted simultaneous and timely use of division intelligence by several elements of the division in various operational areas and allowed for rapid updating of information to be passed to other headquarters.

In addition to its own computer effort, the 25th Infantry Division took advantage of many outside computer operations. A typical example was the division's use of the computer-generated MACV Hamlet Evaluation System.

INTERIOR OF UNIVAC 1005 COMPUTER VAN

Another major activity at Cu Chi was the intensive Army aircraft maintenance program. All divisions in Vietnam required this massive effort, and each division base camp devoted a major portion of its area and resources to aircraft maintenance. Lieutenant General Julian J. Ewell in his debriefing report wrote:

> Aircraft maintenance is the most important single area in the division, due to the fact that the tempo of operations is dependent to a large degree on a high aircraft availability rate. With a fixed base system as in Vietnam, one can optimize the aircraft maintenance system (hangars, hardstands, lights, etc.) and achieve peacetime availability rates under combat conditions. We flew the fleet 90 hours per month per aircraft (and were edging up to 100 hours) and kept the availability rate over 80%. Hueys and Cobras could be kept up in the high 80's. This required a virtuoso maintenance performance with iron control over every aspect of both aircraft operations and maintenance.

The aircraft maintenance program in Vietnam started at the top with the 34th General Support Aviation Maintenance and Supply Group, which provided limited depot-level maintenance, general support, backup direct support maintenance, and supply support for all Army aircraft in Vietnam. Support was also given for airframe, power-plant, armament, and avionics repair. From early 1965 the 34th General Support Aviation Maintenance and Supply Group grew to four aircraft maintenance and supply battalions with a total of ten direct support and five general support companies, because the number of aircraft increased from 660 in 1965 to over 4,000 in late 1968. Backup maintenance was given to both the division maintenance units and the 1st Aviation Brigade. The brigade, in turn, provided supplemental logistic and tactical airlift throughout Vietnam.

Concepts relative to Army aviation in land warfare had never been thoroughly tested in combat; therefore, Vietnam was something of a laboratory for the discovery and development of many innovations in aviation operations. As a report by the Pacific Command on the war in Vietnam states:

> Several actions were taken to speed maintenance and repair procedures. Direct support maintenance detachments were provided to all separate helicopter companies. This additional maintenance capability was immediately reflected by a corresponding rise in aircraft availability rates.

Initially, direct support aircraft maintenance detachments were attached to nondivisional aviation units. Next, many detachments were completely consolidated with the service platoon of the parent aviation company, allowing better use of supervisory personnel. Responsiveness to the aviation unit's over-all flying mission was greatly increased. Studies made in 1966 revealed that for divisional units the number of aircraft available had risen approximately 15 percent. The studies also showed that the maintenance system of the separate aviation units was capable of more complete direct support maintenance than was the conventional divisional maintenance system. The nondivisional units provided, in effect, a one-step maintenance system by integrating organizational and direct support aircraft, avionics, and armament maintenance efforts. A study by the Army Concept Team in Vietnam recommended approval of decentralized direct support aircraft maintenance for all standard infantry divisions in Vietnam. Major General George I. Forsythe in his debriefing report wrote, "Sufficient advantages accrue from the decentralized maintenance concept to warrant implementation at the earliest practical time."

The recovery of disabled aircraft was another mission performed daily by aircraft maintenance units in Vietnam. The 56th Aircraft Direct Support Maintenance Company recovered over 350 downed aircraft in 1968 alone. The former commander of the 56th, Lieutenant Colonel Emmett F. Knight, tells how "Goodnature Six" and many other direct support units accomplished the mission of recovery.

> The aircraft recovery team is organized around the UH-1H. It is the rigging ship and carries the team, tools and equipment required to prepare a downed aircraft for airlift. The rigging ship provides weapons for fire support while on the ground and the necessary radios to control the operation.

RECOVERY OF DOWNED HELICOPTER BY CH-47 CHINOOK

A normal mission might begin with a radio or phone call to the Direct Support Company's operation officer. This request includes all necessary information: type of aircraft, location, extent of damage, security situation, etc. . . . The recovery officer (airlift commander) is notified immediately and begins his planning. . . . He makes a thorough map reconnaissance, does some rapid time-distance planning and places a call to the unit supplying the CH-47 (Chinook). He will pass the mission, including time on station which he has calculated, to the Chinook unit control station.

Meanwhile, the copilot of the rigging ship will have the recovery ship wound up. Takeoff is initiated within minutes after the mission is received. . . . The flight plan is opened and radar monitoring is requested. Artillery advice is checked periodically along the route.

As the flight progresses into the area where the downed aircraft is located, contact is made with the ground forces operating in the area. The troops at the site report on the exact situation as final approach is initiated.

On the ground the rigging crew from the UH-1H begins preparing the downed aircraft for the imminent pickup by the CH-47 which should arrive on the scene momentarily. The pilot of the Chinook receives advice and assistance from the recovery officer while on approach, as the rigging crew completes the hook-up, and during departure from the area. All elements are then notified that the extraction has been completed.

Nearly every aircraft which crashes, is shot down or forced to land in enemy controlled or contested territory will be recovered for repair or salvage. The effort will be coordinated by the aircraft maintenance direct support unit.

Between 1965 and 1971, the CH-47 (Chinook) rescued downed aircraft worth approximately $2.7 billion.

A related innovation which helped to sustain the number of division aircraft available was the development and use of a floating aircraft maintenance facility. This facility was a Navy seaplane tender converted into a floating depot for aircraft maintenance. The ship, the USNS *Corpus Christi Bay*, arrived on station in Vietnam on 1 April 1966. By July production reached 34,000 man-hours per month of manufacturing, disassembling, repairing, and rebuilding operations. During fiscal year 1969, a total of 37,887 components valued at $51.9 million was processed. Ninety-one percent were returned to serviceable condition. The 34th General Support Group reports indicate that the floating aircraft maintenance facility alone was responsible for an additional 120 aircraft available daily in Vietnam.

In the final analysis, the base camp and its many facilities were many things to many people. It was a "Holiday Inn" to the soldier in the field and a base of operations for the logisticians. It represented a drain on resources of the combat commander, but it permitted the aircraft mechanic to do his job. It was a phenomenon of the area war.

CHAPTER XIV

VINH LOC and PHU VANG I (September 1968)

Two operations of the Vietnam War, VINH LOC and PHU VANG, illustrate how the Vietnamese paramilitary forces were combined with U.S. forces in activities aimed at the destruction of the Viet Cong infrastructure. The U.S. Army has a long history of operations with the regular military forces of allies. However, the extended association of U.S. regular units with indigenous paramilitary organizations was new to the Army and required a succession of innovations in many aspects of operations.

The World War II association of U.S. units with the Philippine Constabulary (a paramilitary force) paralleled the situation with the Vietnamese paramilitary forces. However, the Philippine Constabulary had been inducted into the U.S. Army Forces, Far East, a few months before the war, and the command relationship was therefore relatively uncomplicated.

As U.S. armed forces, other than advisory groups, joined the Vietnamese conflict, they were superimposed on the existing Vietnamese military structure. The U.S. units began operating in areas assigned to the Vietnamese corps tactical zone commanders, who had subdivided their areas among their assigned divisions of the Army of the Republic of Vietnam. This arrangement, of course, created problems of area responsibility and co-ordination. To complicate these problems further, the provincial (sector) and district (subsector) political partitions of the country had several indigenous paramilitary organizations under the control of the province and district chiefs.

In addition to the need to integrate all units into combat operations, there was a compelling requirement to train the indigenous forces to do the jobs themselves. Major General Melvin Zais, commander of the 101st Airborne Division (Airmobile), in his debriefing report outlined the problem and its solution.

> It became apparent from the earliest days of my command that in order to insure a lasting success in our operations against the enemy forces in Thua Thien Province the troopers of the 101st Airborne Division must fight side by side with the GVN [Government of Vietnam] forces. To this end every

operation of any significance was a combined operation with 101st Airborne units and 1st ARVN Division and/or Province units. To insure close coordination US and ARVN command posts were co-located for operations, and liaison was established with the 1st ARVN Division headquarters and regimental headquarters, Province headquarters and every district headquarters in Thua Thien.

This collocation of units, together with the concept of "tactical areas of interest," insured co-ordination between forces. In the long run the system served to strengthen the South Vietnamese forces, including the paramilitary units. It proved to be tremendously effective as American commanders worked with the Vietnamese commanders to increase the competence, confidence, and aggressiveness of indigenous troops.

Vinh Loc Island is approximately twenty-five miles long and three miles wide at the widest point. It is situated in Thua Thien Province along the coast of the I Corps Tactical Zone fifteen miles east of Hue. Before the 1968 Communist *Tet* offensive, the island was relatively secure under South Vietnamese government control and the 50,000 inhabitants were unmolested by the Viet Cong. During *Tet*, however, the attention of allied forces was diverted away from areas such as Vinh Loc to more populated areas. This diversion allowed the enemy to infiltrate, gain control of the island, and use it as a haven. As a result, many of the inhabitants fled.

During the spring and summer of 1968 several one- and two-day operations were conducted to destroy the enemy force. Each resulted in enemy losses but failed to uproot the Viet Cong infrastructure. An analysis of these efforts revealed that a longer operation using available Vietnamese resources together with U.S. forces was needed to clear the island. A combined planning group was therefore established consisting of the province and district chiefs, Vietnamese Army commanders, U.S. advisers, and the commanding officers of the 2d Brigade, 101st Airborne Division (Airmobile), and the 1st Battalion (Airmobile), 501st Infantry. The 2d Brigade was commanded by Colonel John A. Hoefling, and Lieutenant Colonel Jim I. Hunt commanded the 501st Battalion. The plan developed by this group called for a combined operation to conduct a soft cordon on the island. The soft cordon differed from a normal cordon operation in several respects. Most significant were the emphasis on combined operation, the limited use of firepower in order to keep property damage and civilian injury at a minimum, and the slow, painstaking searches by the sweeping and cordon forces.

Phase I of the plan consisted of positioning the ground blocking forces on D minus 1 (10 September 1968) in such a way that the enemy would believe that all the activity was just an extension of normal operations. Company D, 1st Battalion, 501st Infantry, conducted an operation in the northwestern part of the island to force the enemy toward the southeast. Concurrently, the 2d and 3d Battalions of the 54th ARVN Regiment moved into blocking positions along the northeastern shore of Phu Vang District to add depth to the river patrol on the estuary between Vinh Loc and Phu Vang.

Phase II began on D-day (11 September) at first light when the naval forces surrounded the island. Immediately thereafter, the 3d Troop of the 7th ARVN Cavalry conducted a reconnaissance in force from the northwest into Vinh Loc District to prevent the enemy's escape and to force him into the cordon. With all blocking forces in position, units of Task Force 1-501 and 1st Battalion, 54th ARVN Regiment, air-assaulted into six landing zones along the seaward shore. From these positions the two battalions began reconnaissance in force operations to the southwest into the blockade established by the 2d and 3d Battalions, 54th ARVN Regiment, and the naval forces. The 922d and 955th Regional Force Companies, previously positioned in their zones between the two battalions, conducted similar sweeps. These maneuvers were quickly executed and were completed on D-day. During the night, the operation involved maximum illumination and engagement of enemy forces attempting to escape the island by water.

Phase III began on D plus 1 (12 September) and continued to the end of the operation on 20 September. This phase consisted of continuous reconnaissance in force activities, saturation patrols, "eagle flights," and night ambushes by all units in assigned areas of operation. The plan was to conduct methodical, detailed searches and to react immediately to combat intelligence gained, while maintaining the cordon around the island.

Indigenous paramilitary forces were used extensively in order to take maximum advantage of their capabilities. The two Regional Force companies were assigned their own areas and conducted operations alongside the ARVN and U.S. rifle companies. Popular Force platoons were positioned with each company-size tactical unit to take advantage of their knowledge of the terrain and the local population. Twenty-four members of the National Police Special Branch, 100 members of the National Police Field Forces, 30 men organized into Armed Propaganda Teams, and a 7-man detail for census grievances were spread throughout the tactical elements to question and control the population. This arrangement insured that South Vietnamese government representatives were with all units, thus minimizing misunderstandings with detainees and allowing a meaningful initial screening of the people.

A central collection point was established where prisoners of war and detainees could be held. Fourteen National Policemen of the district were responsible for the security and handling of suspects

ARVN SOLDIERS AND U.S. ADVISER

brought to the collection point. Near this facility was a Combined Intelligence Center, where representatives of all U.S. and Vietnamese intelligence agencies were located. Through the workings of a combined staff, the initial interrogation produced information that was used within minutes. The Provincial Reconnaissance Units (ten 12-man teams) reacted immediately to exploit specific intelligence, and People's Self-Defense Forces were used wherever possible in searching the villages. In one village, twenty members of the People's Self-Defense Force joined ten U.S. troopers in a combined air assault in reaction to intelligence.

The Vietnamese at the Combined Intelligence Center were quick-witted and capitalized on available opportunities. For example, helicopters carrying 231 suspects landed at the interrogation center between 0100 and 0230 hours on 12 September. The landing zone was dusty and noisy, and the suspects were considerably confused. As the helicopters were unloaded the suspects were given directions such as, "All members of K4B Battalion over here, C117 Company over there." Accordingly, sixty-three of the suspects lined up as directed. The district S-2 then asked the suspects to identify other members of their units who had not followed the instructions. In this way, more prisoners were identified.

The over-all operation was extremely successful. Before the operation began, two enemy companies reinforced with hamlet guerrillas were estimated to be in the area. At the completion of the operation, enemy organizations were virtually ineffective and the regular U.S. and ARVN forces were replaced by Regional and Popular Forces. Subsequently, two revolutionary development teams returned to the area and continued their work with no further interference.

PRISONERS OF WAR ARE TAKEN TO COLLECTION POINT

The VINH LOC operation was followed by Operation PHU VANG I in an area near the Vinh Loc district boundary. The operational area was approximately one kilometer east of Hue city and included parts of three districts. The area within the cordon, approximately twenty-nine square kilometers completely surrounded by navigable waterways, was along the primary infiltration route into the city.

During the four months before the operation, numerous contacts were made with two- to five-man enemy groups. The enemy was active, employing numerous mines and booby traps along the canal on the north and east of the eventual cordon. The area was known to have a strong and deeply rooted Viet Cong infrastructure. The civilian population feared the Viet Cong and as a result they tried to avoid all allied forces and seldom gave information about the enemy. Under these circumstances, a prolonged operation including a detailed search of the area was needed. Calling on the experience gained on Vinh Loc Island earlier in the month, planning was done by a combined staff and envisaged the use of all available U.S., ARVN, province, and district resources.

The operation included three phases. Phase I began on D-day (27 September 1968) with all forces conducting diversionary operations to deceive the enemy and, if possible, to force him into the cordon area. Task Force PHU VANG and Task Force HUONG THUY moved into assigned areas just east of Hue early in the morning. Colonel Hunt's 1st Battalion, 501st Infantry, was placed in the area north and northeast of the cordon, while Task Force 2-17 moved into blocking positions on the southern edge of the cordon to seal off escape to the south. In the meantime available naval forces screened adjacent waterways, and a composite battalion of the 54th ARVN Regiment swept from the southeast toward the cordon area.

Phase II called for most of the available forces to move overland and close into blocking positions around the cordon area by 0730 hours on D plus 1 (28 September). Company A, 1st Battalion, 501st Infantry, air-assaulted into its blocking position. Shortly thereafter, 2d Battalion, 54th ARVN Regiment, air-assaulted into two landing zones in the western portion of the cordon, swept to the east to engage any large enemy force encountered, and detained all suspicious persons.

The final phase began on D plus 2 (29 September). All forces conducted detailed searches within their areas, rapidly exploiting new intelligence.

In execution the operation went as planned with one exception. Information obtained through interrogation of detainees early on 27 September indicated that the enemy would attempt to withdraw from the cordon to the east before blocking positions could be established in the area. Consequently, the cordon was closed immediately instead of waiting until 28 September.

Once again maximum use was made of available indigenous paramilitary forces. Regional Force companies participated in the operation in their own assigned areas. Popular Force platoons served as blocking forces and contributed their knowledge of the area and local population. National Police Field Forces, Police Special

Branch, Provincial Reconnaissance Units, and Census Grievance Teams were spread among the tactical forces to assist in the initial screening of the people and the questioning of the detainees. They also worked at the Combined Intelligence Center, processing information gained from detainees for immediate exploitation.

Although the immediate tactical results of these two battles were impressive, the long-term results of the VINH LOC and PHU VANG I operations were even more significant. Viet Cong control was replaced by South Vietnamese government control and a new environment of stability. U.S. and ARVN tactical units were replaced by Regional and Popular Forces and eventually People's Self-Defense Forces.

The VINH LOC and PHU VANG cordons are excellent examples of combined operations conducted on a basis of co-ordination and co-operation between the forces of two countries. These soft cordon operations were characterized by surprise, combined planning, combined operations and intelligence centers, minimum destruction, population control, rapid reaction to intelligence, and detailed searches. The combined tactical operations center, where the operational representatives of all elements were located, was essential for these operations. Normally the commanders were also at the combined centers. This system enabled better co-ordination, control, and planning and achieved unity of command.

The Combined Intelligence Center also contributed significantly to the operations. Representatives of all intelligence agencies—U.S., Vietnamese, military, paramilitary, and civilian—participated in the interrogation system. This practice insured that the resources of each agency were used to the best advantage and the unique abilities of each of the forces in the cordon area were exercised without delay to exploit intelligence as it became available.

Another significant aspect of the soft cordon was the limited supporting fire. This precaution was necessary because of the presence of friendly units and individuals inside the cordon. Strict fire discipline had to be imposed on all participating units, but civilian casualties and property damage were kept at a minimum because of it.

The success of the VINH LOC and PHU VANG operations came from many factors: soft cordon tactics, combined planning, combined operations and intelligence centers, and the widespread integration of South Vietnamese paramilitary units and civilian agencies into U.S. formations. These combined operations, in addition to defeating the enemy, had a lasting effect on the area. They uprooted the Viet Cong infrastructure in Vinh Loc and Phu Vang and contributed significantly to the confidence and aggressiveness of the Vietnamese forces.

CHAPTER XV

Search and Destroy

Among the most important differences between the war in Vietnam and earlier wars was the effect of U.S. military operations on the people in the theater. In earlier wars, U.S. commanders were charged with the humane treatment of civilians and with minimizing the impact of their units' operations on the people. In Vietnam this obligation became more important than in any previous war. Winning over the hearts and minds of the people was fundamental to the U.S. effort; therefore, U.S. commanders were necessarily involved in helping the people to achieve a new life.

The increased involvement of military commanders with the local population led to many innovations in the war. The 1st Infantry Division's "county fair" operation was an excellent example of an effective response to a population control problem that was new to U.S. commanders. Another and more far-reaching innovation was the operational terminology developed to express the new relationship between military operations and the people. The three most basic operations or missions were search and destroy, clearing, and security. These terms and the concepts they described were new, and like most new names and ideas, they were understood by some and misunderstood by others. Best known and most misunderstood was search and destroy. Some insights into the conflict about search and destroy operations can be gained by relating them to other operations and to the strategy as it developed during the war.

In Vietnam, conventional operations were described in traditional military terms. For example: the 1st Squadron, 1st Cavalry, defended critical installations at Tam Ky; the 11th Armored Cavalry provided convoy security at Suoi Cat; and the 1st Brigade, 5th Mechanized Division, interdicted enemy routes on the Khe Sanh plateau. Securing, clearing, and search and destroy operations, however, were unique to the war in Vietnam.

Search and destroy operations began in 1964, before U.S. ground forces were committed. These operations were conducted to locate the North Vietnamese Army and Viet Cong main force units in and around their base areas and to attack them by fire and maneuver. Since enemy infiltration of the populated areas depended heavily on the availability of base areas near the population centers, destruction of close-in base areas received priority attention.

The mission to search for and destroy the 5th Battalion, 95th NVA Regiment, carried out by the 2d Battalion (Airborne), 502d Infantry, exemplified many search and destroy operations of the war. The activities of the 1st Brigade, 5th Mechanized Division, on the Khe Sanh plateau were also search and destroy operations even though the brigade's mission included interdiction of a North Vietnamese Army infiltration route.

The second of the three basic missions was clearing. Clearing operations were conducted to drive enemy forces away from populated areas and to allow small units to carry on securing activities among the people. These operations upset the pattern of mutual support that was essential to the enemy's integrated main force-local force effort. Operation IRVING demonstrated the clearing of the central coastal area of Binh Dinh Province and the effects of the operation on the inhabitants.

Securing operations, the last of the three missions, were directed at the enemy in the hamlets—at the infrastructure and the farmers by day and at the Viet Cong guerrillas by night—who operated individually as well as in squads and platoons. These enemy elements required tactics that were different from those used against the main forces. Saturation patrols and squad-size ambushes, which were highly risky in the jungle against the main forces, proved to be effective against the local guerrillas. During securing operations, U.S. and allied forces maintained a respect for private property and for the people whose hearts and minds were the objectives of the enemy forces. An example of securing operations were those conducted by the 101st Airborne Division (Airmobile) mentioned earlier.

Each of the three missions supported the pacification program, but to a different extent. Securing operations directly supported pacification and required close and continuous integration of military and civilian efforts. Clearing operations indirectly supported pacification and required a lesser degree of co-ordination with civilian agencies. Search and destroy operations generally required no co-ordination with civilian agencies. They were aimed at destroying the enemy's main forces in uninhabited areas and in his base areas, his logistic resources in particular.

Under some circumstances in Vietnam the distinction between the types of operations was extremely important. For example, when units, especially large units, moved into new areas the definitions were essential. They were the basis for each element's understanding its own tasks and the tasks of neighboring units. They were particularly important to government civilians in establishing the relationships between their agencies and the military forces.

After units had been in operational areas for a time and had established working relationships with other government agencies in the vicinity, the classification of day-to-day operations became less important. An example is the 1968 battle of Loc Ninh near the Cambodian border, in which the 1st Infantry Division was involved. The mission was the defense of Loc Ninh. The enemy's attack on the district headquarters provided a tactical opportunity to destroy a major part of the 9th Viet Cong Division. The 1st Infantry Division responded to the need to defend Loc Ninh and seized the opportunity to engage the Viet Cong division. To the extent that the battalions of the 1st Infantry Division denied the enemy access to the several thousand people living in and near the district town, their activities were clearing operations. To the extent that the battalions' objective was the destruction of the enemy's forces, their operations were search and destroy. The lack of a precise distinction between clearing and search and destroy operations resulted in many clearing operations being reported as search and destroy and contributed to the misunderstanding of the terms. Another contributing factor was the identification of all three missions as search and destroy in the 1968 Combined Campaign Plan. The necessary distinction between the three was finally made by describing securing as search and destroy (local), clearing as search and destroy (provincial), and combat operations against the main forces in the uninhabited areas as search and destroy (regional).

Regardless of the terms, all three missions contributed to the same objective, that is, a sense of security and confidence for the South Vietnamese people. Since these operations competed for the same resources, senior commanders in Vietnam were required to achieve and constantly adjust a balance between them. The principal variables that influenced the balance were intelligence, weather, terrain, and availability of trained troops and support. Some knowledge of the changes that affected these variables during the different phases of the war is essential to an understanding of the shifting balance.

Four phases of the Vietnam strategy have been described by General Westmoreland. All four phases emphasized strengthening the Republic of Vietnam armed forces. In addition, during the first phase, from mid-1965 to mid-1966, the enemy offensive was blunted. The second phase, from mid-1966 to the end of 1967, saw the mounting of major offensives that forced the enemy into defensive positions and drove him away from the population centers. In phase three, beginning in early 1968, the Vietnamese armed forces were additionally strengthened, and more of the war effort was turned over to them. (*Chart 1*) The final phase called for further weakening of the enemy and strengthening of the Army of the Republic of Vietnam as the U.S. role became, in the words of General Westmoreland, "progressively superfluous."

CHART 1 — THREE PHASES OF VIETNAM STRATEGY

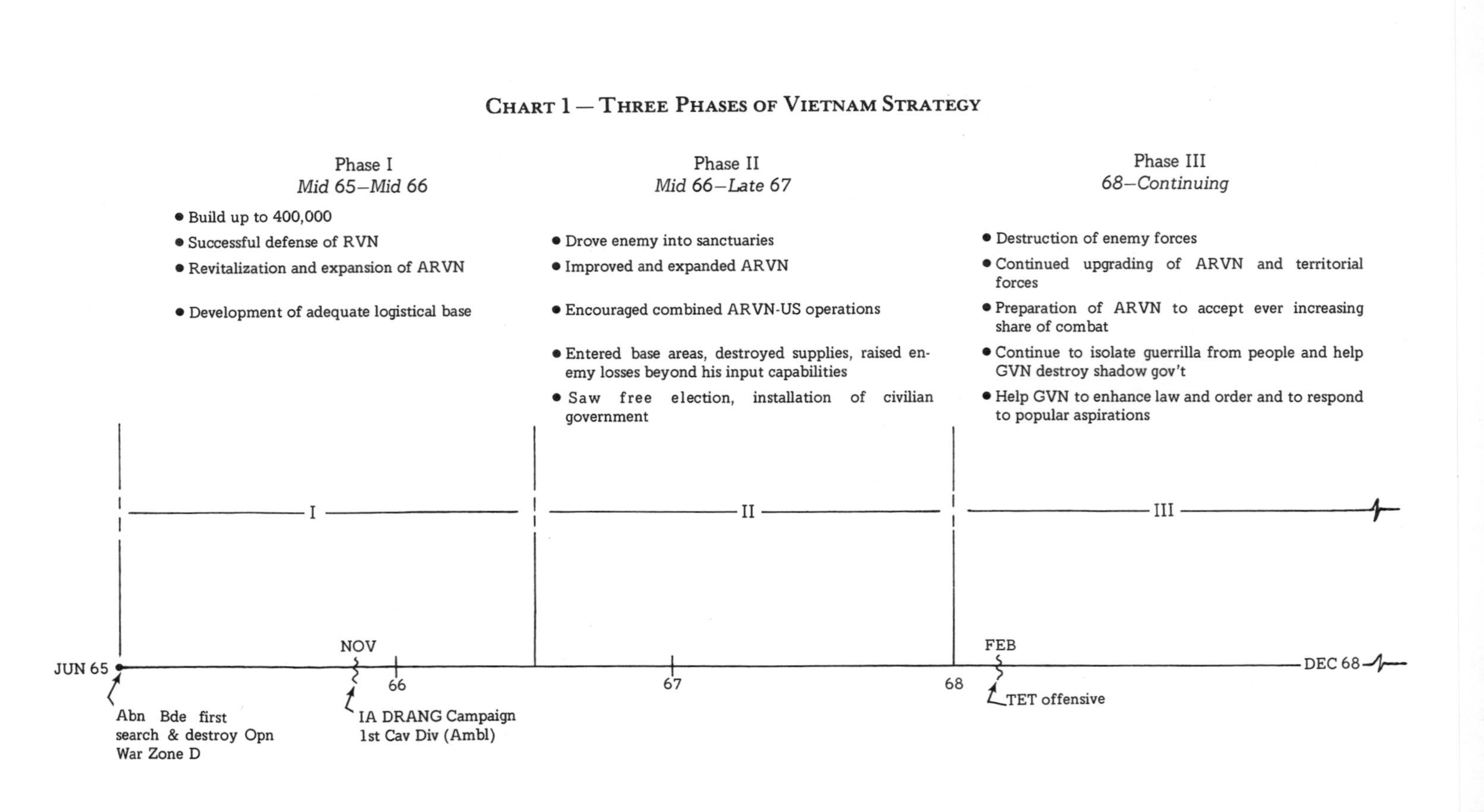

The central reality of the first phase was the threat to the existence of South Vietnam posed by the Viet Cong main force units and the North Vietnamese Army. The threat was apparent in late 1964 and in early 1965, when Viet Cong tactics took a more menacing turn. During the battle for Binh Gia, a small village southeast of Saigon, the 9th Viet Cong Division stood and fought for four days and inflicted heavy casualties on the Republic of Vietnam forces. This action was a significant change from the enemy's normal hit-and-run tactics. The battle and a series of large-scale actions in the Mekong Delta in early 1965 pointed toward the enemy's escalation to the third step of Mao Tse-tung's formula for insurgencies: major combat by organized military forces. The situation in 1965 was further illustrated by the Communists' stated objectives: "strangulation of the Republic of Vietnam (RVN) at its narrow waist south of Hue; seizure of one or more provinces in the central highlands and establishment of an autonomous, Communist-controlled government; . . . [and isolation of] Saigon, the political capital and military nerve center, from the rest of the country."

The commitment of U.S. forces in 1965 prevented the enemy from attaining his objectives and averted collapse in the south. In this environment of impending disaster U.S. units were first ordered to search for and destroy or neutralize North Vietnamese Army and Viet Cong forces, base areas, and supply points. During this phase of the U.S. troop commitment, the U.S. 1st Cavalry Division (Airmobile) fought the battle of the Ia Drang Valley. The 1st Cavalry Division decisively defeated three North Vietnamese Army regiments and killed over 3,500 enemy soldiers in thirty-five days. In this and subsequent battles in which major U.S. formations were committed, the aim was to blunt the enemy offensive and gain time for the South Vietnamese to rebuild their forces. By the end of the first phase, the enemy threat had been offset by the improvement in the South Vietnamese armed forces and the continued buildup of U.S. forces. (*Chart 2*)

The beginning of the second phase was signaled by a re-establishment of a military balance and a clear indication that the initiative was passing to the allies. This phase was a period of developing strength and accelerating effort. The strategy became one of a general offensive and the maximum practical support of the Revolutionary Development Program. Since the U.S. forces were uniquely qualified for area warfare, they were given the mission of carrying the battle to the enemy's main forces, while ARVN concentrated its efforts on revolutionary development, a task for which it was far better suited than U.S. troops. Although over half the U.S. combat force during 1967 was employed in or near the populated areas, spoiling attacks and search and destroy operations in the enemy's base areas were a

INFANTRY TROOPS SEARCHING ENEMY BASE AREA

fundamental part of the strategy. Search and destroy continued as a principal operation, and the time spent in search was generally in proportion to the validity of the ever-improving intelligence concerning the enemy.

Early in the second phase, the U.S. command was faced with the dual requirements of maintaining an offensive against a substantial enemy threat gathered in the base areas and in sanctuaries across the Cambodian and Laotian borders and, at the same time, providing security to protect the pacification program. Operations CEDAR FALLS, JUNCTION CITY, and MANHATTAN illustrated how the balance between offensive operations and local security operations was achieved northwest of Saigon in early 1967.

CEDAR FALLS was a clearing operation in the Iron Triangle just north of Saigon. The 1st Infantry Division, the 173d Airborne Brigade, the 11th Armored Cavalry, elements of the 25th Infantry Division, and several ARVN units sealed off and searched the base area, which had served as a logistic base and headquarters for the Viet Cong's Military Region IV. The operation, which lasted for nineteen days during January 1967, resulted in 720 enemy killed, 213 enemy captured, and hundreds of tons of rice destroyed or confiscated. Equally important were the discovery and destruction of a vast underground headquarters and the capture of thousands of pages of enemy documents. The real success of the operation lay, however, in the disruption of enemy plans for the Saigon area, a disruption that permitted a significant acceleration in the pacification program in areas close to the capital.

Chart 2 — Vietnamese and Allied Forces in South Vietnam

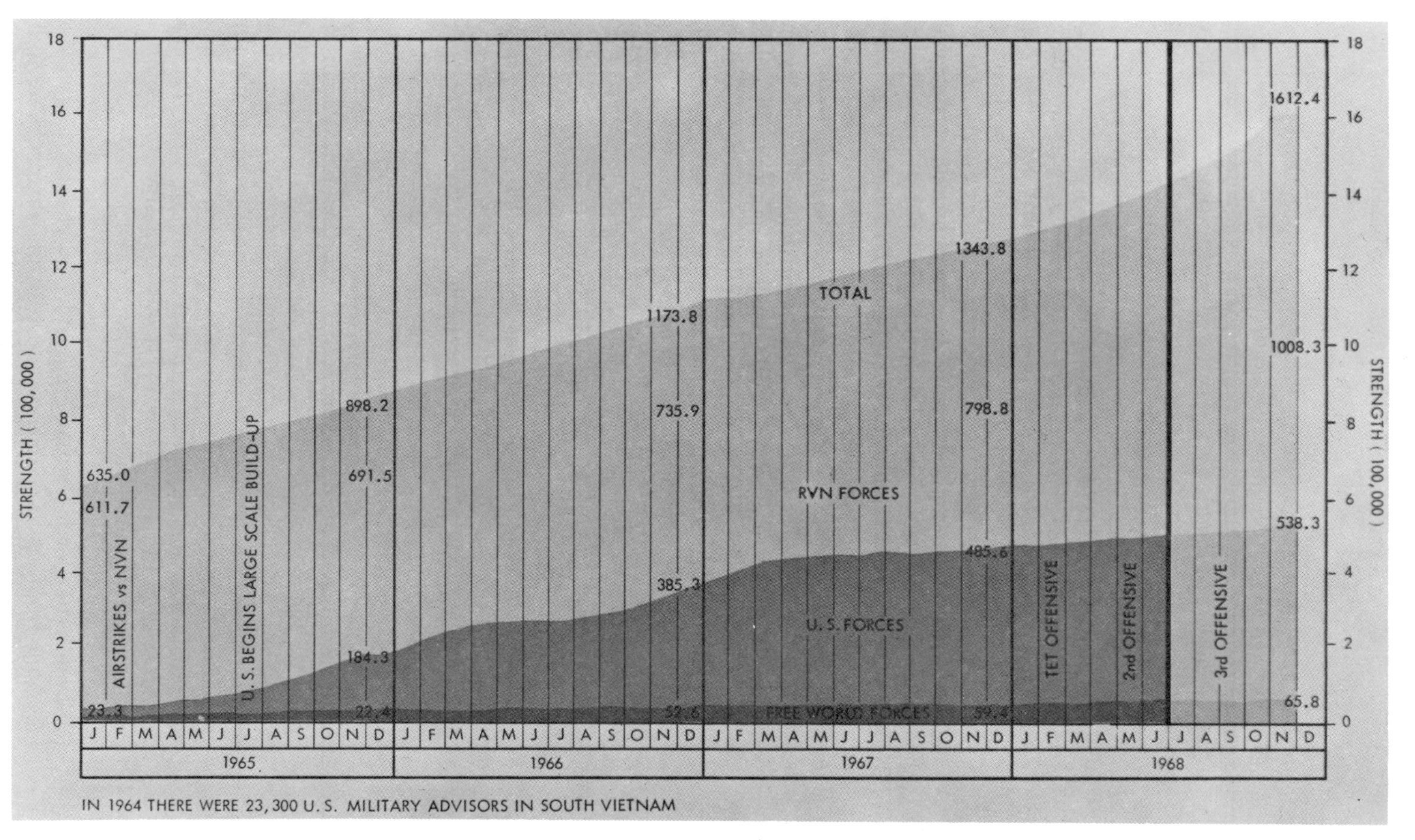

JUNCTION CITY was a search and destroy operation begun in February 1967 by the 1st and 25th Infantry Divisions, the 11th Armored Cavalry, the 173d Airborne Brigade, the 196th Light Infantry Brigade, elements of the 4th and 9th Infantry Divisions, and several ARVN units. JUNCTION CITY, the largest operation of the war until that time, brought the battle to the enemy in the War Zone C sanctuary, which had been virtually unchallenged before. The operation lasted until mid-May and resulted in over 2,700 enemy killed. In addition, to prevent the enemy from rebuilding his base by making U.S. re-entry into War Zone C relatively easy, three C-130 airstrips were built and two Civilian Irregular Defense Group camps were established in what had been clearly recognized as enemy-held territory.

Operation MANHATTAN immediately followed JUNCTION CITY. Elements of the 1st and 25th Infantry Divisions, the 11th Armored Cavalry, and ARVN forces conducted clearing operations in the Long Nguyen base area north of the previously cleared Iron Triangle.

CEDAR FALLS, a clearing operation, JUNCTION CITY, a search and destroy operation, and MANHATTAN, also a clearing operation, were typical of U.S. efforts to insure a balanced strategy, striking out at the enemy in his border base areas periodically but returning to zones near the population center in order to maintain a secure environment for the pacification program.

Both clearing and search and destroy operations were essential to the war effort. Pacification could not proceed unless the enemy's main forces were defeated or held at bay in their sanctuaries. As Lieutenant General Richard G. Stilwell wrote: "Large unit operations . . . [were] the precondition for the shield behind which proceeded all other actions to bring security to the people. With the big battalions isolated, the remaining and smaller elements of the total communist structure [could be] subjected to widespread attack by something approaching saturation tactics."

As the second phase drew to a close, less than 50 percent of all U.S. combat elements were deployed against the enemy's main forces in his base areas. Most U.S. forces were directed against the guerrillas and local forces. This distribution of forces, which had been maintained throughout 1967, caused the enemy to revise his tactics. He was convinced that keeping his main forces close to major population centers was no longer a tenable tactic and that he must make more use of the Cambodian and Laotian sanctuaries. In fact, from base areas in Cambodia, the enemy prepared for his 1968 *Tet* assault against Saigon, thirty miles away. (It was 1970, however, before U.S. entrance into these sanctuaries was authorized.)

In September 1967, General Vo Nguyen Giap predicted heavy fighting as the North Vietnamese decided to change their tactics, to move out from the sanctuaries, and to bring their waning military power to bear on the government and people of South Vietnam: to deal a knockout blow no matter what the cost.

The third phase of the war began in early 1968. Although the objectives of the second phase included wearing down the enemy and driving him away from the population centers, they did not take into consideration that the enemy was a victim of his own propaganda, that he was irrational, or that he was prepared to pay an awesome price to enter the cities of South Vietnam. Enemy losses from the beginning of the *Tet* offensive until the end of February 1968 far exceeded the total U.S. losses in the war up to that time. In this single offensive, the Communists lost 45,000 men killed in action—more than the U.S. losses in the entire Korean War. Clearing operations increased significantly during and after *Tet*. U.S. units were committed in the populated areas to oppose the enemy units that had penetrated and in the uninhabited areas to block the enemy's withdrawal and to prevent reinforcement of his battered forces. By June 1968 the enemy's losses resulting from these and the other allied operations were estimated to be 170,000 men. By the end of 1968 the level of security known to the South Vietnamese people before *Tet* had been restored.

As the third phase progressed, more U.S. forces were committed to missions supporting the pacification program. Even in the northernmost corps zone, the only zone in Vietnam where enemy main force battalions outnumbered friendly battalions, the 101st Airborne Division (Airmobile) was able to commit two of its nine battalions exclusively to the pacification effort. Other battalions, although they continued to operate in the mountains in mobile defense of the populated seacoast area, supported specific districts. This support took various forms, for example, continuous liaison, training teams, civic action support, and quick reaction operations of company and battalion size.

Early in the third phase the U.S. command recognized that the term "search and destroy" had unfortunately become associated with "aimless searches in the jungle and the destruction of property." In April 1968 General Westmoreland therefore directed that the use of the term be discontinued. Operations thereafter were defined and discussed in basic military terms which described the type of operation, for example, reconnaissance in force. Besides avoiding the misunderstanding of search and destroy operations, the change expressed the difference between U.S. operations in the early stages of the war and those conducted during the third phase. In the early stages, the terms "clearing," "securing," and "search and destroy" had served as doctrinal teaching points to show the relationship between military operations and the pacification effort. They had been adopted in 1964 for use by military and civilian agencies involved in pacification. By 1968, when the terms were dropped, the pacification program had developed to the point where civilian-military co-ordination was routine. Vietnamese and Free World field commanders understood the capabilities and limitations of the civilian agencies, and the civilians had a similar grasp of the military contribution.

Search and destroy operations, by any name, were the tactics by which U.S. units engaged the enemy. They were the right operations at the time, and they contributed to the essential function of shielding the pacification effort from the enemy's main forces. Without the shield, the South Vietnamese would not have had the opportunity to rebuild their forces, and the pacification effort in Vietnam would have been impossible.

CHAPTER XVI

Summary

This monograph demonstrates that Vietnam was a war of innovations. The contestants, the equipment, the arena, and the rules of engagement were different from previous wars. In the beginning, there was a great variety of recently developed hardware but a general lack of doctrine concerning insurgency-type operations. Improved equipment was rushed through the development phase, and successful ideas originated in the field. Some of the innovations described in the preceding chapters are peculiar to the Vietnam situation, while others represent more significant advances that can be used in future conflicts.

Many of the major innovations in Vietnam were time-sensitive, that is, they were effective only for a given period of time. This period could best be measured as the time required for the enemy to figure out what the Americans were doing and to develop effective countermeasures. Sound innovations lasted for long periods of time, and some are as valid today as when they were conceived. Others were useful for days or weeks or for a few months only. The enemy soon punished the commander who followed set patterns or precise procedures. The innovative leader usually met with success.

The widespread use of the helicopter was the most significant advance of the Vietnam War. Combined with a new air-assault concept, it led to the refinement of the airmobile division that proved to be an unqualified success, incorporating all the advantages that the helicopter provided. It is difficult to exaggerate the capabilities of the airmobile team in Vietnam; the team represented the most revolutionary change in warfare since the blitzkrieg. However, airmobile tactics may also be time-sensitive, and the helicopter has problems with respect to future application.

Improvements in communications paralleled or even exceeded the progress made in mobility. Not since before the Civil War has a brigade commander been able to see and talk to all his platoon leaders. The division commander had an abundance of hot lines, secure voice radios, and instant communications up the chain of command, down to every tactical unit, and across to other services or allies. Compared the EE-8 and SCR-300 of Korea, communication equipment in Vietnam was a technological miracle of infinite value to the commander.

Firepower progressed along with mobility and communications. The infantry soldier had a greater variety of more powerful weapons than ever before. Artillery and armor pieces were more mobile and more effective. Aerial fire support increased many times, and much of it was available from among the Army's own resources. Furthermore, the role of firepower expanded from one of softening the enemy in preparation for the final infantry assault to one of entirely eliminating enemy resistance.

The sensors, target acquisition equipment, and night observation devices, combined with the automatic data processing equipment, represent a major advance in military systems management at the battalion level and higher. Development of such equipment has progressed rapidly within the U.S. Army. As a result, there is high expectation for improved intelligence-gathering methods and a more efficient use of combat power. The G-2 and G-3 (intelligence and operations assistant chiefs of staff) will not only be in the same tent in the future, they will also use the same computer.

In the field of tactics, the age-old principles did not change. U.S. forces conducted a huge mobile defense for over five years. They fought off the invader from fixed bases; however, in doing so they used almost purely offensive tactics. An intelligence network superior to anything known in previous wars and great tactical mobility allowed the U.S. forces to pre-empt most of the enemy's meticulously rehearsed plans. The riverine operations, the ambushes, logistic support of armored formations by air, and the saturation patrolling demonstrated that the commander at every level was equal to the task of outthinking the enemy.

Contact with the enemy was normally made by battalions or smaller units in contrast to the larger unit operations of World War II and Korea. In Vietnam, U.S. infantry on the ground had the mission of finding the enemy by means of saturation patrolling and never-ending reconnaissance in force, guided by a whole new world of intelligence-gathering sensors and air cavalry. Having found the enemy, invariably at less than 100 yards range, the infantry commander called forth overwhelming reinforcement and firepower. The main attack was wherever and whenever the enemy could be found.

The air cavalry, armored cavalry, tanks, and mechanized infantry all proved their versatility and effectiveness in low-intensity warfare against an unsophisticated enemy. The battles reported throughout the monograph show these forces seeking out and destroying the enemy at close quarters. The U.S. armored vehicles and armed helicopters, dedicated to the offensive, were well suited to overwhelming the enemy's hidden light infantry.

The adaptation of U.S. forces to the countrywide battlefield evolved through a process of trial and error. Not since the American Revolution has a theater of operations been occupied with friendly and enemy military forces in the same general areas simultaneously. Success was not clear-cut; control of the population was often in doubt; victory or defeat lay at the grass-roots level after the maneuver battalions had done their work. Thus, there were two wars going on: the purely military battle against the enemy's main force and the pacification operation. The two were completely entwined, however, and the commander at every level fought in both.

Pacification was an unprecedented addition to the commander's mission. Although it was basically a civilian endeavor, the military played a vital and continuous part because the restoration of security in the countryside was a prerequisite to pacification. Furthermore, the local Vietnamese administration was often almost wholly military in character and was dependent upon the Americans for necessary skills and equipment. Winning the war meant winning the hearts and minds of the people, and all friendly forces participated in this effort.

Vietnamization of the war, which later received a great deal of publicity, actually started with the first advisers and progressed through increasing U.S.-Vietnamese co-operation. It was always the goal of U.S. forces to leave behind in Vietnam an indigenous force able to defend itself. Specific units from each country were paired up, not only to insure co-ordination but also to provide cross-training. Vietnamization took its place alongside pacification and military operations as a primary mission of the U.S. commander.

There was one area, however, where American ingenuity failed: countermine warfare. Considering the magnitude of the enemy's effort in mines and booby traps, U.S. experts failed to find the answer to the problem of how to counter them. Another aspect of the war in Vietnam which many tactical commanders would revise was the large base camp. Because of the size to which these camps grew, they detracted far too much effort from the primary combat mission.

Finally, the question might be asked: Has the U.S. Army been successful in Vietnam? Certainly the United States has not been victorious in the traditional sense. But in 1965 ARVN units were being beaten in every quarter of the country. The South Vietnamese government had lost control of most of the countryside. Total defeat was imminent. By the early 1970s most of the major U.S. Army formations had come to Vietnam, made their contribution, and been withdrawn. As a result, the ARVN has become one of the most powerful military forces in the Free World, and the Republic of Vietnam now controls the majority of its people. (*Chart 3*) The U.S. Army in Vietnam carried on its traditions of ingenuity, imagination, and flexibility. It kept pace with the hectic technological progress of today's

Chart 3 — Population Status in South Vietnam

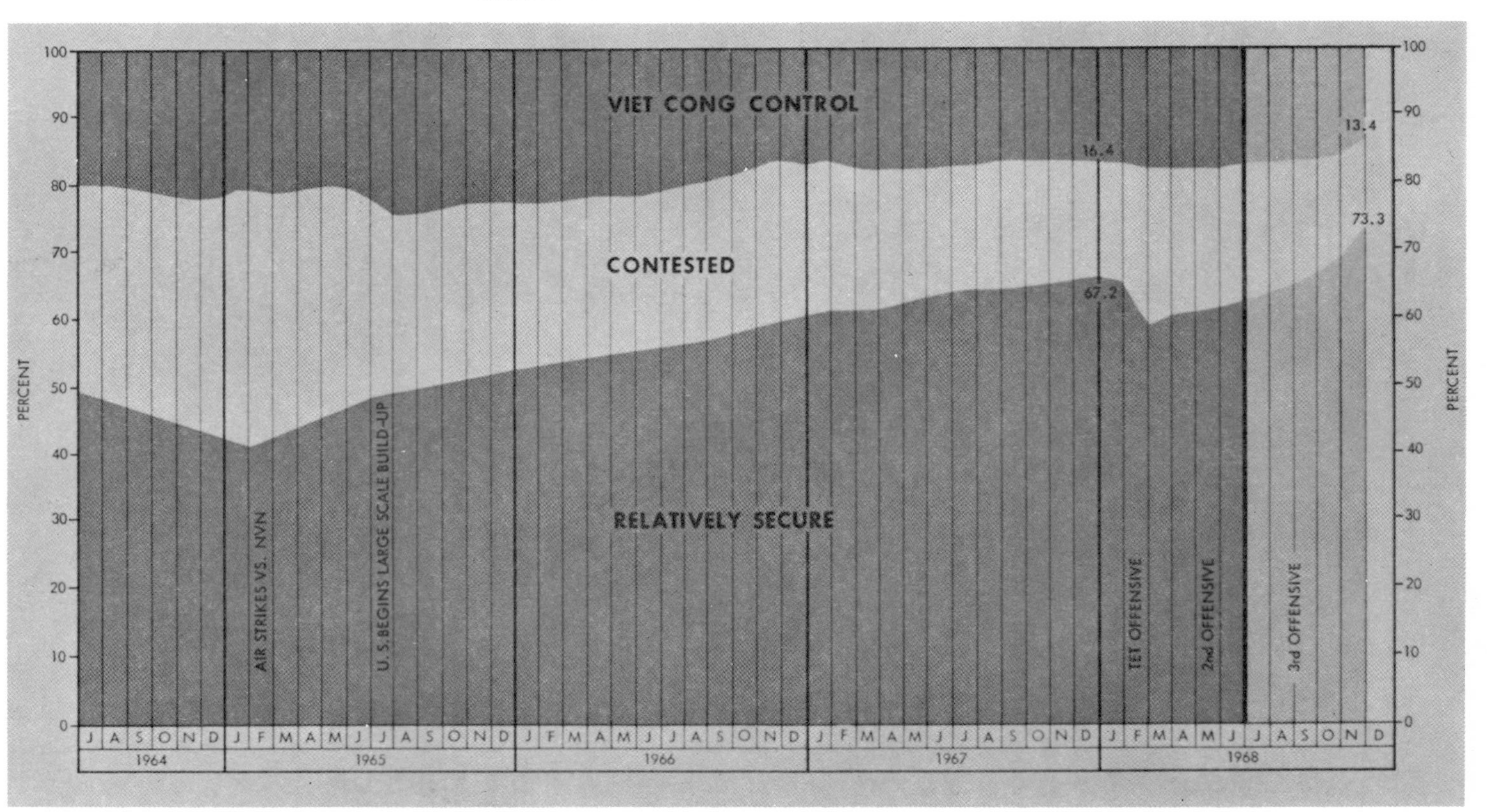

world and demonstrated the American soldiers' ability to outthink the enemy. It showed its sophistication in materiel advances, its strength of will in guerrilla warfare, and its compassion in pacification.

Glossary

AAAS	American Association for the Advancement of Science
ACAV	Armored cavalry assault vehicle
ACV	Air cushion vehicle
ARA	Aerial rocket artillery
ARVN	Army of the Republic of Vietnam
AVLB	Armored vehicle launched bridge
BIRMINGHAM	Operation conducted in April 1966 by the 1st Infantry Division in War Zone C near the Cambodian border in Tay Ninh Province
CAISSON VI	Fire base of 1st Infantry Division near Xa Cat
CEDAR FALLS	Joint clearing operation in January 1967 conducted by 1st and 25th Infantry Divisions, 173d Airborne Brigade, 11th Armored Cavalry, and ARVN units against VC Military Region IV headquarters in the Iron Triangle
CEV	Combat engineer vehicle
CIDG	Civilian Irregular Defense Group
CN	Type of tear gas
CORONADO X	Operation in which the Mobile Riverine Force responded to Viet Cong attacks on My Tho and Vinh Long, drove the enemy from those provincial capitals, then operated near Cai Lay on Highway 4, early in 1968
CROOK	Fire support base in Tay Ninh Province established in April 1969
CS	Riot control type of tear gas
DELAWARE	Operation conducted in spring of 1968 by U.S. and ARVN units into A Shau Valley to pre-empt enemy preparations for an attack on the Hue area
DSU-GSU	Direct support unit-general support unit
FLOYD	Fire support surveillance base constructed in 1970
G-3	Assistant chief of staff for operations and training at an army, corps (field force in Vietnam), or division headquarters

G-4	Assistant chief of staff for supply and evacuation at an army, corps (field force in Vietnam), or division headquarters
G-5	Assistant chief of staff for civil affairs at an army, corps (field force in Vietnam), or division headquarters
Hue City	Operation early in 1968 conducted by U.S. Marine Corps and ARVN elements to defend and drive the enemy from Hue city during the *Tet* offensive
Huong Thuy	Task force composed of U.S. and Vietnamese forces involved in Operation Phu Vang I
Ingram	A task force consisting of the 2d Battalion, 12th Cavalry, reinforced with a battery of artillery. The task force was charged with the security of Pleiku and the support of ARVN operations at Plei Me during the early stages of the battle for Ia Drang in 1965.
Irving	Operation conducted by the 22d ARVN Division, the Republic of Korea Capital Division, and the U.S. 1st Cavalry Division (Airmobile) against 610th NVA Division in Binh Dinh Province in October 1966
J-2	Assistant chief of staff for military intelligence, MACV
J-3	Assistant chief of staff for military operations, MACV
Junction City	Largest operation conducted in Vietnam at the time, involving twenty-two U.S. and four ARVN battalions in War Zone C (Tay Ninh Province) and bordering provinces, 22 February–14 May 1967
Lam Son II	Combined pacification operation conducted in June 1966 by Headquarters, 1st Infantry Division Artillery, and Headquarters, 5th ARVN Division, in Tan Phuoc Khanh
LRP	Long-range patrol
MACV	Military Assistance Command, Vietnam
Manhattan	Clearing operation conducted in 1967 by the U.S. 1st and 25th Infantry Divisions, the 11th Armored Cavalry, and ARVN forces in the Long Nguyen base area just north of the Iron Triangle
Masher–White Wing	Operation conducted early in 1966 by 1st Cavalry Division (Airmobile), ARVN, and South Korean forces in Binh Dinh Province
MEDCAP	Medical Civic Action Program

MONTANA MAULER	Operation in April 1966 in the central demilitarized zone involving elements of the 1st Brigade, 5th Infantry Division (Mechanized), as well as U.S. Marine Corps units
NCR	National Cash Register
NIAGARA FALLS	Operations conducted early in 1968 by U.S. air and artillery to counter the enemy buildup against Khe Sanh
NVA	North Vietnamese Army
PAUL BUNYAN	Massive jungle-clearing project conducted by specially trained Army engineer units in September 1966
PERMACAP	Personnel Management and Accounting Card Processor
PHU VANG	Task force composed of U.S. and Vietnamese forces involved in Operation PHU VANG I
PHU VANG I	Operation conducted in September 1968 by U.S. forces and Vietnamese paramilitary forces in an area one kilometer east of Hue city that included parts of three districts
PSYOP	Psychological operations
RANCH HAND	Operation to conduct defoliation and anticrop activities
REMAGEN	U.S.-ARVN armored-mechanized task force with Marine Corps units sent in March 1969 by the XXIV U.S. Corps commander to the Khe Sanh plateau to open Route 9 to Khe Sanh, cut Route 926, and protect the west flank of a 3d Marine Division reinforced regiment, which was trying to prevent the enemy from moving across the lower end of the plateau toward the A Shau Valley
RPG	Rocket-propelled grenade
S-2	Officer in charge of the military intelligence section of a brigade or smaller unit
S-3	Officer in charge of the operations and training section of a brigade or smaller unit
S-5	Officer in charge of the civil affairs section of a brigade or smaller unit
SHENANDOAH II	1st Infantry Division operation in Binh Duong Province and extended to include Loc Ninh area of Binh Long Province after the enemy attacks on the district town, 27 September-19 November 1967
THAYER I	Operation in September 1966 in which U.S., ARVN, and

Korean units forced the 610th NVA Division into a natural pocket, thus setting the stage for Operation IRVING

UNIONTOWN III-BOXSPRINGS — Operation conducted in February-March 1968 around Bien Hoa and Xuan Loc, northeast of Saigon

USARV — U.S. Army, Vietnam

USNS — United States Navy ship (civilian manned)

VC — Viet Cong

VINH LOC — Operation conducted in September 1968 by U.S. forces and Vietnamese paramilitary forces to free Vinh Loc Island from enemy control

YELLOWSTONE — 25th Infantry Division operation in War Zone C (Tay Ninh Province), 8 December 1967-24 February 1968

Index

A Shau Valley: 57-58, 64
Aerial rocket artillery (ARA): 12, 15, 180. *See also* Fire support; Helicopters; Rocket, aerial, 2.75 folding-fin, M3.
A-frame: 113
AGILE project: 90
Air Assault Division, 11th: 10, 16
Air cavalry: 10, 15-17, 108, 124
Air Cavalry Squadron, 12th: 85
Air cushion vehicle (ACV): 76-77
Air Force, Seventh: 91
Air lines of communication: 58-60, 86
Air operations, tactical: 8, 12, 30, 43, 45, 47, 49, 71-72, 78, 100, 110, 120, 155. *See also* Aircraft.
Air supply: 6, 11, 22, 58-60, 62, 155. *See also* Helicopters.
Airborne Brigade, 173d: 51, 78-80, 84-85, 91, 101, 103, 174, 176
Airborne Division, 82d: 143
Airborne Division (Airmobile), 101st: 20, 33, 56, 84, 117, 124, 143, 146, 162-64, 170, 177
Airborne Infantry Regiments
- 327th: 20
- 501st: 163, 167
- 502d: 117-18, 120, 124, 126, 170
- 503d: 79, 91

Airborne reconnaissance platforms: 5
Aircraft. *See also* Air operations, tactical; Bombing operations.
- AC-47 ("Spook"): 27, 100, 129
- AC-119: 100
- airborne radio relay: 84
- armed, development of: 14
- B-26: 15
- B-52: 27, 32
- C-47: 120, 122
- C-123: 11, 20, 90
- C-130: 176
- CH-54 ("flying crane"): 28
- CV-2 (Caribou): 11, 22-23, 84
- CV-7 (Buffalo): 11, 22-23
- ground protection of: 41
- herbicide missions: 90, 94
- maintenance, recovery, and repair: 148, 151, 158-61

Aircraft—Continued
- OV-1A (Mohawk): 14
- safety precautions for: 32
- surveillance: 22
- T-28: 15
- YO-3A (Quiet): 22

Aircraft Direct Support Maintenance Company, 56th: 159
Airmobile operations: 10, 29-30, 32, 41, 179-80
Airmobility concept: 3, 6, 10, 13-16, 56
Ambush Alley: 127
Ambush operations: 3, 13, 20-21, 52-53, 75, 88, 91-92, 95, 105, 123, 127, 130, 134, 136, 155, 180
American Association for the Advancement of Science (AAAS): 94-95
American Embassy, Vietnam: 91
Ammunition, 7.62-mm: 51, 75, 114
Ammunition, beehive: 103
Ammunition, canister: 114-15
Ammunition supply: 86-87
An Khe: 10-11
An Loc: 115
Ann Margaret Dam: 149
Anticrop operations: 89-94
Anti-intrusion devices: 42, 52-53
Armor
- 34th: 113
- 69th: 114-15
- 77th: 57-58, 64

Armor employment: 110-16, 127-28, 130-31, 136, 180
Armored Cavalry, 11th: 111-12, 115, 127-30, 132, 135-36, 169, 174, 176
Armored cavalry assault vehicle (ACAV): 110-12, 127-28, 130, 135
Armored cavalry employment: 107-16, 180
Armored personnel carriers: 9, 111, 115-16, 133
Armored Reconnaissance Airborne Assault Vehicle, M551 (Sheridan): 9, 21, 111-12, 115-16
Armored Vehicle Launched Bridge (AVLB): 57-58, 64
Army marksmanship training unit: 75

Army of the Republic of Vietnam (ARVN): 171, 173, 182
- Airborne Battalion, 2d: 79-80
- Airborne Battalion, 3d: 79-80
- Cavalry, 7th: 59, 164
- Census Grievance Teams: 164, 168
- Corps, I: 56
- Corps, II: 11
- Corps, III: 54-55
- Division, 1st: 56, 163
- Division, 5th: 137, 140
- Division, 22d: 24-25
- National Police units: 164, 167
- paramilitary forces: 162-68
- People's Self-Defense Force: 165, 168
- Popular Force troops: 76, 164-65, 167-68
- Provincial Reconnaissance Units: 165, 168
- Ranger forces: 38
- Regiment, 7th: 137-38
- Regiment, 42d: 79
- Regiment, 54th: 164, 167
- Regional Force units: 164, 167-68

Arnett, Peter: 36
Artillery
- 4th: 57, 63
- 6th: 53-54
- 11th: 99
- 15th: 48
- 19th: 11, 20, 27-29
- 20th: 28, 33
- 30th: 120
- 34th: 67-69
- 35th: 130
- 77th: 105

Assault boats: 27
Assault Helicopter Companies: 15
- 48th: 20
- 129th: 20
- 179th: 20

Attack helicopter companies: 15
Automated battlefield management systems: 3, 9, 156, 180
Automatic data processing systems: 9, 148, 156-57, 180
Aviation Brigade, 1st: 159
Aviation Company, 92d: 11

Ba, Lieutenant Colonel: 140-41
Ba Bep: 148
Ba Rai River: 69
Ban Me Thuot: 8
Barges: 73, 77
Base camp construction and operations: 21-22, 31, 148-61, 180, 182
Battlefield illumination: 20-21, 27, 52, 100, 120, 122, 164. *See also* Flares; Searchlights.
Bell, Major Walter C.: 131
Bell Aerosystem air cushion vehicle: 76
Ben Cui Rubber Plantation: 112
Ben Het: 79
Bien Hoa: 124
Binh Chuan: 137
Binh Dinh Province: 24, 29, 101, 170
Binh Duong Province: 138-39
Binh Gia: 173
Binh Son Rubber Plantation: 87
BIRMINGHAM operation: 54
Bland, Lieutenant Colonel Ivan C.: 68
Body snatch operations: 17-18
Boi Loi Woods: 92
Bomb, chemical, BLU52: 38
Bomb, 10,000-pound, M121: 39
Bombing operations: 8, 24, 27, 30, 32, 41, 78. *See also* Air operations, tactical.
Booby traps: 111, 130-33, 157, 167, 182
Bulldozers: 99, 104, 112-13
Bunker, Ellsworth: 92
Bunker lines: 104, 109, 149
Bunker Use Restriction Bomb (BURB): 37

Ca Lu: 58, 64-65
Cai Cam River: 70
Cai Lay: 69-70
Cambodian border sanctuaries: 6, 12, 98, 104, 174, 176
Camp Dong Tam: 67, 69
Camp Enari: 86
Camp Evans: 63
Camp Holloway: 11, 86
Cargo slings: 63-64
Casualties: 27, 29-31, 43, 49, 51, 68, 70, 73, 122, 128-31, 173, 177
Casualties, enemy: 12-13, 20, 27-29, 43, 46-49, 51, 59, 68-70, 73, 76-78, 101, 103, 110, 112, 115, 121-22, 124, 129, 155, 173-74, 176-77
Caudill, Captain Watson G.: 42-43
Cavalry
- 4th: 112, 137-38, 148
- 5th: 26, 28, 57, 60
- 7th: 25, 27
- 8th: 11-13, 25, 34, 79
- 9th: 12-13, 20, 25-27
- 12th: 11-12, 25-27, 30, 79-80
- 17th: 107

Cavalry Division (Airmobile), 1st: 10-12, 15, 20, 24-25, 27-29, 36-37, 39, 78-79, 84-85, 105, 111, 143, 169, 173
Cavazos, Lieutenant Colonel Richard E.: 42-43, 47, 51
CEDAR FALLS operation: 89, 174, 176
Checkerboard search tactics: 118-19, 126
Cholon: 38
Chu Pong Mountain: 12-13
Chua Chan Mountain: 127-28
Circe wheel code: 85
Civic action: 24-25, 143, 146, 177
Civil affairs operations: 141-43, 146
Civil Operations and Revolutionary Development Support (CORDS): 91
Civilian Irregular Defense Group (CIDG) camps: 10-11, 47-48, 117, 176
Civilians: 132-33, 139-43, 169-70, 178, 182
Claymore mines. *See* Mines.
Clearing operations: 169-71, 176-77
Clemons, Sergeant Richard F.: 119
Cloverleaf reconnaissance formation: 42-43, 45
CN gas: 36, 38
Cochran, Lieutenant Colonel James F., III: 48
Codes: 85
Combat Aviation Battalion, 10th: 20
Combat Engineer Vehicle (CEV), M728: 112-13, 115
Combat Support Helicopter Company, 228th: 63
"Combat trap" clearing operations: 39
Combined Intelligence Center, Vietnam: 132, 165, 168
Command and control: 17, 19, 78, 82-84, 120, 122, 126, 135
Communications systems: 9, 78, 80-86, 115, 128, 179-80
Compass, magnetic pilot: 64
Computers: 156-57, 180
Convoy operations: 6, 148, 154-56, 169
Cordon and search operations: 31, 137-42, 163-68, 174
CORONADO X operation: 66-77
Corps, XXIV: 58
Corps Tactical Zones: 162
  I: 163
  II: 10
  III: 22, 127, 131, 134
  IV: 22
Corpus Christi Bay: 161
Cousland, Lieutenant Colonel Walter C.: 107-10
Crittenberger, Brigadier General Willis D., Jr.: 54
Crusher, transphibian tactical: 87
CS munitions: 34, 36-38
Cu Chi base camp: 148-58
Cyclone fence: 109, 116

Da Nang airfield: 63
Da Yeu: 42, 45-46
Dak Hodrai Valley: 79
Dak To: 78-96, 124
Daniel, Colonel Charles D.: 25
Darlac Province: 80
Dau Tieng: 154
David, Colonel Bert A.: 67, 70
De Saussure, Brigadier General Edward H.: 150
Deception tactics: 74, 95, 97, 99, 117-18, 120, 122-23, 126
Defoliation operations: 39, 89-95
DELAWARE operation: 64
Delta project: 123
Detectors, personnel: 72, 78, 80, 105, 124
Di An: 42
Dietrich, Lieutenant Colonel Frank L.: 117-18, 120, 122
Dinh Tuong Province: 68, 70
Dogs, use of: 34, 42-43, 45, 133, 136, 141
DSU-GSU system: 156
Duc Co Special Forces Camp: 13
Dust control agents: 41
Dust-off medical evacuation: 39-41

Eagle flight tactics: 16, 164
Eagle float operations: 70, 77
Emerson, Lieutenant Colonel Henry E.: 118
Engineer Battalions
  7th: 64
  8th: 28, 34, 39, 41
  14th: 64
  26th: 113
  27th: 89
  28th: 129
  35th: 89
  62d: 89
  65th: 149
  86th: 89
  93d: 87
  168th: 89
Engineer Brigade, 20th: 88

Engineer operations. *See also* Tunnel clearing operations.
base camp construction: 150-51
bridging: 113
construction equipment: 28, 39
fire base construction: 19, 103-04
land clearing: 87-89, 132
landing zone construction: 38-39, 41
mine clearing: 131
ENSURE 202 Tank-Mounted Expendable Mine Roller: 134
"Evaluation of Mechanized and Armor Combat Operations in Vietnam (MACOV)": 115
Ewell, Lieutenant General Julian J.: 76, 158

Fairchild Aircraft Corporation: 51
Fairfield, Lieutenant Colonel Ronald J.: 114
Field Artillery Data Computer: 156
Field Force, I: 54, 60, 114
Field Force, II: 54, 148
Field Forces, Vietnam: 11
Fire support: 9, 12, 42-45, 47, 49, 53, 78, 105, 130, 155, 180. *See also* Guns; Helicopters; Howitzers; Mortars.
central tactical control: 54-56
floating artillery platforms: 6, 68-71, 73, 77
herringbone formation: 128, 134-36
interdiction fire: 99, 103
"killer junior" and "killer senior": 100, 103
preparatory fire: 30, 110
safety precautions: 30-31, 54, 168
Fire support, enemy: 3, 8, 99-100, 107-08, 128, 130, 148-49, 155
Fire support bases: 6, 8, 47, 91, 97, 106, 148, 154
ALABAMA: 68
CAISSON VI: 103
CROOK: 98-101, 103-05
FLORIDA: 68
FLOYD: 101, 103-05
GEORGIA: 68
Flamethrowers: 48-49
Flares: 11, 20, 22, 30, 52, 105, 120
Floating aircraft maintenance facility: 161
Folson: 25
Forsythe, Major General George I.: 159
Fort Benning, Georgia: 75
Fort Campbell, Kentucky: 124
Foster, 1st Lieutenant Nathaniel W.: 53-54
Fuel containers: 60, 86

Gas. *See* CN gas; CS munitions.
General support companies: 15
General Support Group, 29th: 154
General Support Group, 34th: 158-59, 161
Gia Ray: 127-28
Giap, General Vo Nguyen: 176
Gibson, Lieutenant Colonel Edward C.: 149
Gibson, Colonel James M.: 57
Gliders: 22
Grenade Launcher, M79: 9, 38, 51-52, 64
Grigg, 1st Lieutenant Donald E.: 26
Gunboats: 6
Guns
90-mm. tank: 111-12
152-mm.: 111
165-mm. demolition: 113
175-mm.: 54

Hacia, Major Joseph E.: 99
Hamlet Evaluation System: 157
Hamlet festival operations: 139-42, 169
Hawk Hill: 107-08
Hay, Major General John H., Jr.: 47
Helicopters: 3, 6, 14, 179
AH-1G (Cobra): 15-18, 21, 33, 72, 148, 158
base camp defense: 21-22
body snatch operations: 17-18
CH-21 (Shawnee): 15-16
CH-46 (Marine): 59
CH-47 (Chinook): 15, 20, 38, 59, 84-86, 91, 104, 160-61
command and control role: 17, 19, 83-84, 120, 122, 126
deception tactics: 74, 95, 117-18, 120, 123, 126
Dust-off medical evacuation: 39-41
eagle flight tactics: 16, 164
eagle float operations: 70, 77
gunship fire support role: 8, 10, 12-20, 22-24, 27, 29-30, 32-33, 43, 45, 47-49, 71-72, 100, 120, 128, 136, 148, 155, 180
heavy equipment and weapons transport: 39, 41, 53, 84
herbicide missions: 90-91
illumination system (Lightning Bug--Firefly): 20
intelligence missions: 17-18, 23
jitterbug and seal operations: 72-74, 77
light observation: 16-18
maintenance, recovery, and repair: 19, 78, 86, 148, 151, 158-61

Helicopters—Continued
medical evacuation role: 10, 22-24, 27, 38-41, 95, 123-24
mortar patrol operations: 22
nap-of-the-earth flight: 20
night operations: 13, 19-22, 26-27
OV-1C (Mohawk): 20
personnel detection missions: 72, 80
psychological operations: 26-27, 41, 143
scout: 12-13, 16-18, 23, 72
security missions: 16, 18, 45
smoke screening missions: 95
supply missions: 22-24, 27, 38, 57-60, 62
teams: 16-19
troop carrying missions: 13, 15, 23-24
UH-1 (Huey): 9, 32-33, 59, 62, 86, 108, 158
UH-1A: 15-16
UH-1B: 15, 20
UH-1C: 22, 95
UH-1D: 20, 84
UH-1D/H (Nighthawk): 21, 100
UH-1H (utility): 16-18, 22, 159-61
Herbicide Assessment Commission (AAAS): 94-95
Herbicide Review Committee: 92
Herbicides: 78, 89-95
Highway 1: 127-28
Highway 333: 128
Hill, Lieutenant Colonel: 69-70
Hill 10: 107
Hill 34: 108
Hill 350: 117, 119-20
Hill 450: 117-22
Hill 875: 80
Ho Chi Minh Trail: 57
Hoa Hoi: 26-27, 30
Hoa Nhut: 142
Hoai An District: 101
Hoefling, Colonel John A.: 163
Holborn, 1st Lieutenant Alden J.: 119
Hollis, Major General Harris W.: 31, 157
Howitzers: 8, 28-29, 33
105-mm.: 17, 20, 73, 99, 103, 130
155-mm.: 53-54, 103, 120, 130
eight-inch: 54, 103, 130
Howze Board: 10
Hue: 163, 166-67, 173
HUE CITY operation: 38
Hue-Phu Bai airfield: 63
Hull: 25
Hung Loc peninsula: 28
Hunt, Lieutenant Colonel Jim I.: 163, 167
HUONG THUY task force: 167
Hyle, Colonel Archie R.: 25-26

Ia Drang: 10-23, 173
Image Intensification System, AN/ASQ-132: 22
INFANT (Iroquois Night Fighter and Night Tracker): 22
Infantry battalion organization: 125
Infantry Brigade, 196th: 176
Infantry Brigade, 199th: 124
Infantry Divisions
1st: 37, 42-53, 56, 82, 84, 87, 89, 97, 103, 115, 137, 141, 143, 146, 169, 171, 174, 176
4th: 75, 78-79, 85, 124, 143, 176
5th (Mechanized): 57-58, 60, 63, 65, 85, 169-70
9th: 66-77, 87, 176
23d (Americal): 85, 107, 113
25th: 97, 99, 148, 150-57, 174, 176
Infantry Regiments
8th: 79
11th: 57, 59-60
12th: 49, 79
18th: 42-43, 47-48, 51, 56
21st: 108-10
22d: 99-100
26th: 48-49, 137
28th: 47-48, 56
47th: 67-70
51st: 124
60th: 67-70
61st: 57-59
Infrared locating devices: 20-21, 76, 97, 105, 133-34
INGRAM task force: 11
Intelligence operations: 5, 17, 25, 117, 124 137, 139, 157, 164-68, 174, 180
Iron Triangle area: 36, 89, 174, 176
Iroquois Night Fighter and Night Tracker (INFANT) system: 22
IRVING operation: 24-41, 170

Jitterbug and seal operations: 72-74, 77
Johnson, 1st Lieutenant George P.: 43
Joint General Staff, Republic of Vietnam armed forces: 90-91
Joint U. S. Public Affairs Office (JUSPAO): 91
JUNCTION CITY operation: 97, 174, 176
Jungle penetrator system: 123-24

Jungle-busting techniques: 112, 116
Junk fleet: 25

Kaczor, Captain George R.: 107
Khe Sanh plateau: 57-58, 64-65, 169-70
Kim Son valley: 24, 28, 38
King Ranch land clearing concept: 87
Kinnard, Major General Harry W. O.: 11
Knight, Lieutenant Colonel Emmett F.: 159
Kontum: 79, 86-87
Kontum Province: 78-79
Korean units: 24-25, 41
Korean War: 3, 8, 10, 30, 32, 53, 80, 82, 122, 126, 151, 177, 180

Lai Khe: 88
Lam, Lieutenant General: 56
LAM SON II operation: 137-42
Land clearing operations: 87-89, 132
Landry, Captain John R.: 128
Laotian border operations: 57, 64, 174, 176
Larsen, Major General Stanley R.: 11
Laser target designator: 22
Latrines, precut kits: 150
LCM (landing craft, mechanized): 73
Leaflets: 25, 27, 139, 144-46
Lichtenberger, Captain Robert: 43
Lightning Bug-Firefly Helicopter Illumination System: 20
LINCOLN operation: 20
Loc Ninh: 42, 45-51, 56, 88, 171
Lockheed Missiles and Space Company: 22
Logistical Command, 1st: 154
Long Binh: 87, 151, 154
Long Ho River: 69
Long Khanh Province: 127
Long Nguyen: 46, 176
Loudspeakers: 26-27, 121-22, 137, 143-44
LST (landing ship, tank): 67
"Lug-a-lug" water container: 63

MACARTHUR operation: 79, 87
McCall, 2d Lieutenant Ralph D.: 43
McFadden, Captain Mike: 119
McGuire rig: 123
Machine gun, .50-caliber: 14, 103, 111, 114, 135
Machine gun, M60: 52, 109, 111, 135
McNamara, Robert S.: 36
Mahone, Colonel Nelson A., Jr.: 33
Maintenance Battalion, 725th: 156
Major Army Subordinate Command Management Information System (ASMIS A): 156
MANHATTAN operation: 154, 174, 176
Mann, Major William M., Jr.: 42
Mao Tse-Tung: 173
Marine Corps units
  Marine Amphibious Force, III: 60
  Marine Division, 3d: 57-58, 60
  Marine Engineer Battalion, 11th: 64
  Marine Logistics Support Unit: 62
  Marine Regiment, 5th: 38
  Marine Regiment, 7th: 36
Marshok, 1st Lieutenant John A., Jr.: 119
MASHER-WHITE WING operation: 37
Masks, protective: 34, 72
Mayer, Captain Frederick F.: 26
Mechanized infantry operations: 59-60, 180
Medbery, Major Wade E., Jr.: 107
Medical Civic Action Program (MEDCAP): 140
Medical operations
  evacuation by helicopter: 10, 22-24, 27, 38-41, 95, 123-24
  treatment of civilians: 137, 140-41
Mekong Delta: 6, 8, 66, 68, 173
Membrane, nylon, T17: 41
Menetrey, Major Louis C.: 47
Meselson, Matthew S.: 94
Milia, Lieutenant Colonel Carmelo P.: 64
Military Pay, Vietnam, system: 156
Military Region IV: 174
Milloy, Major General Albert E.: 143
Mine Warfare Center (USARV): 131-32
Mines: 111, 128, 132, 134, 167
  claymore: 9, 13, 48, 53, 56, 104, 109, 120, 123, 130
  countermeasures: 131, 157, 182
  detection: 45, 133, 136
  nuisance mining: 130
Minh Thanh: 115
Minigun, 7.62-mm., XM-27: 17, 21-22
Mity Mite (Riot Control Agent Dispenser, M106): 37
Mobile floating bases: 67-71
Mobile Riverine Force: 66-71, 77
MONTANA MAULER operation: 57, 60, 62
Mortars: 8, 30, 38, 53, 101, 103, 120
Muller, Brigadier General Henry J., Jr.: 56
My Tho: 68, 70, 77
My Tho River: 67

National Academy of Sciences: 95
NCR (National Cash Register) 500 computer: 156
Nestor program: 85
New York *Times*: 36
Nha Trang: 14
NIAGARA FALLS operation: 89
Nicholson, Lieutenant Colonel Tom M.: 84

Night observation devices: 20-22, 52, 76, 97, 103-05, 112, 115, 134, 164, 180
Night operations: 6, 8, 13, 19-22, 26-27, 47, 50-51, 53, 89, 123
North Vietnamese and Viet Cong units
  Battalion, 5th: 121-22
  Battalion, 261st: 68
  Battalion, 263d: 68
  Battalion, 514th: 68
  Division, 1st: 78
  Division, 3d: 108-10
  Division, 9th: 42, 45-46, 171, 173
  Division, 304th: 59
  Division, 610th: 24
  Local Force Battalion, 72d: 107
  Local Force Company, V-13: 107
  Local Force Company, V-15: 107
  Main Force Battalion, 70th: 107
  Regiment, 2d: 27-28, 101, 103
  Regiment, 24th: 79
  Regiment, 32d: 10, 79
  Regiment, 33d: 10, 12-14
  Regiment, 66th: 79
  Regiment, 95th: 117, 170
  Regiment, 165th: 46
  Regiment, 174th: 79-80
  Regiment, 271st: 42, 46
  Regiment, 272d: 46, 48-49, 101, 115
  Regiment, 273d: 46-49
  Regiment, 275th: 127
Norton, Major General John: 25-26
Nui Mieu Mountains: 25, 27, 34
Nuoc Ngot Bay: 27

Observation towers: 104, 134
O'Connor, Major General George G.: 69
Optical scopes: 101
Overwatch reconnaissance: 45

Pacification: 3, 8, 137, 142, 146, 149, 155, 170, 174, 176-78, 182-83
Parker, Major General David S.: 41
Patrols: 5, 18, 123-26, 180
Pattern analysis: 5
PAUL BUNYAN operation: 89
Pearson, Brigadier General Willard: 123
Peers, Lieutenant General William R.: 78, 114, 124
Peneprime: 41, 132
"People sniffer": 78, 80, 124
Pepke, Major General Donn R.: 75, 143
Personnel Management and Accounting Card Processor (PERMACAP) system: 156
Petroleum products: 60, 86
Phan Rang: 8
Phan Thiet: 114
Philippine Constabulary: 162
Phong Cao: 117-26
Phong Dinh Province: 144
Phu Cat Mountains: 25
Phu Cong: 148
Phu Cuong: 139, 141
Phu Loi Base Camp: 142
PHU VANG operation: 166-68
Phu Xuan River: 108
Phuc, Captain: 140
Phung Hiep District: 144
Pineapple Forest: 107
Plei Me: 10-14
Plei Mrong: 85
Pleiku: 8, 10-11, 87
Polei Kleng: 85
Population control: 25, 41, 169, 182
Propaganda: 92-93, 149, 164
Prothero, Captain Michael B.: 107-08
Provincial Road 6C: 11
Provisional Corps, Vietnam: 60
Psychological operations: 24-27, 41, 121-22, 131, 137, 141-46
Pumps: 60, 62, 86

Quan Loi: 48, 56, 88
Quang Ngai Province: 132
Quang Tin Province: 107

Radar
  AN/PPS-4: 33, 104-05
  AN/PPS-5: 33, 101, 103-05
  ground controlled approach: 63-64
  night vision role: 52, 97, 99-101, 104-05
  radar raids: 33-34
Radio broadcast operations: 25
Radio communications: 82-85, 143
Radosevich, 1st Lieutenant Wilbert: 128, 136
RANCH HAND operation: 90-91
Rations: 8, 123
Recondo operations: 119-24
Reconnaissance in force operations: 31, 134, 180
REMAGEN task force: 58-60, 62-64
Repair parts: 156
Rest and recuperation programs: 149, 151, 161
Resupply operations: 86-87, 154-55. *See also* Air supply; Helicopters.
Revolutionary Development Program: 173

Rifles
M1: 9
M14: 51, 75
M16: 9, 51-52
Riot control agents: 27, 34, 36-38, 72
Riverine operations: 6, 31, 66-77, 166-67, 180
Rocket, aerial, 2.75 folding-fin, M3: 14, 17, 22, 33, 37, 95
Rocket-propelled grenade (RPG) screen: 109, 115-16
Rome plow operations: 21, 87-89, 91, 132, 155
Root, Lieutenant Colonel James T.: 26, 30
Rosson, Lieutenant General William B.: 60
Routes
1: 25, 107, 132
9: 58, 64
13: 88-89
14: 86
92: 57
512: 79
926: 57-58, 64
QL 13: 89
Rung Sat Special Zone: 93-94

Saigon: 6, 8, 173, 176
Saigon Support Command: 154
Salagar, Private First Class Roy: 26
Salzer, Captain (USN) Robert S.: 68
Search and destroy operations: 169-71, 173-74, 176-78
Searchlights: 21, 52, 76, 99-100
Securing operations: 169-71, 174, 177, 182. *See also* Cordon and search operations.
Semiguerrilla warfare: 123
Sensors: 5, 9, 21, 34, 53, 97, 99-101, 103-05, 123, 134, 180
Shaped charges: 104, 109
SHENANDOAH II operation: 51, 89
Sheridan (Armored Reconnaissance Airborne Assault Vehicle): 9, 21, 111-12, 115-16
Shillelagh missile: 111
Signal Battalions
13th: 84
124th: 85
Field Force: 82
Signal Brigade, 1st: 80, 82
Silvasy, Captain Stephen, Jr.: 119
Smoke, tactical use of: 30, 34, 37, 43, 95, 120, 122
Snipers: 74-76, 103
Sniperscope: 52, 75
Soui Ca Valley: 27-28, 38
Soviet weapons: 49
Special Forces Group, 5th: 123
Special Operations Squadron, 12th: 91
Special Warfare Aviation Detachment (Surveillance), 23d: 14
Speech security apparatus: 85
Speed shift howitzer technique: 53-54
Spotting scope, M49: 74
Spray system, C-123/MC-1 (Hourglass): 90
SS11 missile: 28, 33
Starlight scopes: 42, 52, 56, 76, 99, 105
Starry, Colonel Donn A.: 115
Stigall, Lieutenant Colonel Arthur D.: 49
Stilwell, Lieutenant General Richard G.: 176
Strategy and tactics: 3, 5, 127, 171, 173-78
Suoi Cat: 127-36, 169
Supply and Transport Battalion, 25th: 154
Support Command, 25th Division (DISCOM): 153-54

"Tactical areas of interest" concept: 54-56, 163
Tactical operations center: 101, 107, 148, 168
Tam Ky: 107-12, 169
Tan Canh: 79-80
Tan Phuoc Khanh: 137-42
Tanks: 110-11, 113. *See also* Armor employment.
Tap An Bac: 113
Target acquisition: 5, 20-22, 34, 45, 52, 56, 76, 97, 101, 103-05, 112, 115, 133-34, 164, 180. *See also* Sensors.
Target identification: 32, 52, 72
Tax collecting points: 76, 89, 91, 142
Tay Ninh: 98, 113, 154
Tchirley, Fred H.: 94
Telescope sights: 75
Television detection: 22
Tents, precut kits: 150
Terrorism: 3, 142
Tet offensive: 66, 163, 176-77
THAYER I operation: 24
Thieu, Nguyen Van: 45
Thua Thien Province: 162-63
"Thunder run" tank technique: 113-14, 116
Tice, Lieutenant Colonel Raphael D.: 49
Tolson, Major General John J., III: 111
Tractors: 87-89
Tri Tam: 113
Truck, 3/4-ton: 86-87
Tumerong Valley: 79

Tunnel clearing operations: 28, 34-37, 41, 45
Tunnel Explorer Locator System: 34
Tunnel rat teams: 28, 34, 41
Turbine engines: 10
Tuy Hoa: 20, 117

Ullman: 27
UNIONTOWN III-BOXSPRINGS operation: 124
UNIVAC 1005 computer: 156
U.S. Agency for International Development: 91
U.S. Army Aviation Test Board: 11
U.S. Army Combat Developments Command: 134
U.S. Army Computer System Command: 156
U.S. Army Concept Team in Vietnam (ACTIV): 75, 159
U.S. Army Finance and Comptroller Information Systems Command: 156-57
U.S. Army Materiel Command: 134
U.S. Army Military Police School: 45
U.S. Army Pacific Mapping and Intelligence Center: 150
U.S. Congress: 95
U.S. Department of Agriculture: 94
U.S. Department of Defense: 90, 94
U.S. Department of State: 90
U.S. Joint Chiefs of Staff: 36
U.S. Marine Corps: 10, 60. *See also* Marine Corps units.
U.S. Military Assistance Command, Vietnam (MACV): 36, 90-91, 124
U.S. Navy: 25, 27, 30, 67-71, 161, 167
U.S. Pacific Command: 159
U.S. Strategic Air Command: 32
Utility tactical transportation company: 14-16

Valley 506: 24, 103
Van Harlingen, Brigadier General William M., Jr.: 80
Vandergrift Combat Base: 60, 62
Vang Tau: 151
Vehicles, tracked: 6, 8, 58-60, 64. *See also* Armor employment; Armored personnel carriers; Tanks.
Viet Cong infrastructure: 137, 142, 144, 146, 157, 162-68, 170
Viet Cong units. *See* North Vietnamese and Viet Cong units.
Vietnamese Agricultural Service: 141
Vietnamese units. *See* Army of the Republic of Vietnam (ARVN).
Vinh Cu: 148
VINH LOC operation: 162-68
Vinh Long: 69-70, 77
Visual signals: 30, 64, 120, 122

War Zone C: 6, 92, 94, 97-98, 176
War Zone D: 6, 46, 92, 94
Water supply: 62-63
Wells, Captain John W., III: 112
Wereszynski, Major Henry J.: 137-38
Westmoreland, General William C.: 10, 12, 34, 36, 56, 124, 149, 171, 177
Weyand, Major General Frederick C.: 54-55
Williams, Lieutenant Colonel Paul S., Jr.: 115
Wire barriers: 72, 104, 109
World War II: 3, 30, 53, 82, 112, 122, 126, 143, 151, 162, 180

Xa Cat: 103
Xuan Loc: 124, 127, 130

YELLOWSTONE operation: 154

Zais, Major General Melvin: 143, 162

☆U.S. GOVERNMENT PRINTING OFFICE: 1974 O—505-627